All About

VERTICAL ANTENNAS

William I. Orr, W6SAI
Stuart D. Cowan, W2LX

RADIO AMATEUR CALLBOOK
P.O. BOX 2013 LAKEWOOD, NEW JERSEY 08701

Caution: Working on antennas or towers can be dangerous. All warnings on the equipment and all operating and use instructions should be adhered to. Make sure that the antenna is disconnected from the station equipment before you begin to work on it. Make sure that your antenna is not close to power lines, and that it cannot drop on a power line if wires or supports fail. Do not attempt to climb a tower without a safety belt. It is best to work on your antenna with someone who can assist you with tools and will be able to help in the event of a problem or an emergency.

Copyright © 1986 by Radio Publications, Inc.

Published in 1993 by Radio Amateur Callbook
(an imprint of Watson-Guptill Publications,
a division of BPI Communications, Inc.),
P.O. Box 2013, Lakewood, New Jersey 08701

Library of Congress Catalog Card Number: 86-061499
ISBN 0-8230-8710-7

Manufactured in the United States of America

1 2 3 4 5 6 7 8 9/01 00 99 98 97 96 95 94 93

TABLE OF CONTENTS

FOREWORD

The Vertical Antenna: How It Came
From Where It Was
To Where It Is Today

In 1896 a young Italian scientist arrived in England with some mysterious apparatus in his luggage. The customs officials, who had seen nothing like it before, examined it so thoroughly that the delicate apparatus was completely wrecked. This was the inauspicious beginning of a venture that was destined to revolutionize the communication pattern of the twentieth century.

Guglielmo Marconi, however, forged ahead with his unusual experiments and went down in history as the father of radio communication. One of his greatest inventions in this field was the antenna and today a descendant of that early device is known as the Marconi antenna. The inventor had the inspiration of combining an elevated wire used in thunderstorm experiments with his crude spark transmitter. The improvement in performance was magical. Marconi, by systematic experiments, found his radio range was extended immediately from yards to several miles. The addition of a telegraph key to his apparatus created a complete communication system which Marconi patented in 1896--when he was 22 years old.

Marconi continued to improve his wireless system and his vertical antenna has rightfully taken its place in history as a practical device for long distance communication.

This new handbook concerns itself with the vertical antenna in all its popular forms for hf and vhf communication. Computer-derived antenna designs are given for amateur bands and information is provided to allow many of the designs to be used on frequencies falling outside the amateur assignments. Important dimensions are given in both English and Metric systems.

The authors of this antenna handbook started experimenting with vertical antennas in 1934. During five decades they have learned a good deal about these interesting and practical antennas, but there is still much to be discovered. There is no reason why you cannot experiment with, and improve on, the antenna designs in this handbook.

Good luck and good DX!

SENATO DEL REGNO

Rome Italy
25ᵗʰ March 1932

Good luck! —

Guglielmo Marconi

Chapter 1

The Real-life Vertical Antenna

A simple description of a vertical antenna is one whose active element is vertical with respect to the earth's surface, and which radiates a vertically polarized wave (Fig. 1). This representation shows a radio wave travelling out of the page towards the reader. By definition, wave polarization is vertical when the electric field of the wave is perpendicular to the earth. The complete radio wave consists of an interplay of energy between the horizontal magnetic field and the vertical electric field (Fig. 2).

If the position of the fields is reversed, the wave is horizontally polarized. In free space the definition is meaningless, as the earth's surface as a reference does not exist.

In proximity to the earth, polarization is important as the surface of the earth reflects radio waves. The results of this reflection depend upon wave polarization, the height of the antenna above the earth, and conductivity of the earth.

Ground Reflection

A radio wave hugging the surface of the earth is called a surface, or ground wave, and is useful only for short-range communication, as it is eventually absorbed by the earth, or wanders off into space. Absorption is less for longer waves than for shorter ones, and the radio range of ground waves in the

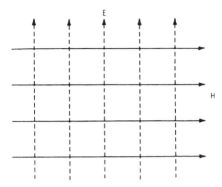

Fig. 1 Head-on view of vertically polarized radio wave. The magnetic lines of force are parallel to the earth and the electric lines of force cut the surface of the earth. The complete wave consists of an interplay of energy between the two force fields.

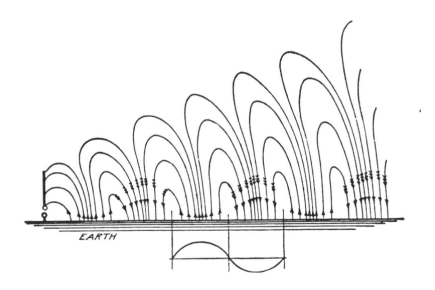

Fig. 2 Early interpretation of a vertically polarized radio wave showing electric field radiated from antenna. (From "Wireless Telegraphy and Telephony", by Ashley and Lewis, 1911.)

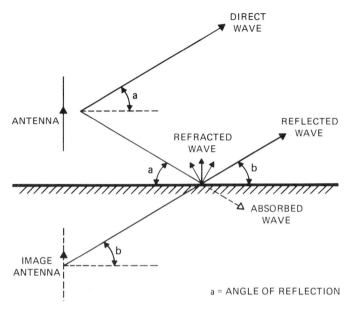

Fig. 3 Reflection of radio wave from vertical antenna above perfect, flat earth. The wave received at a distant point consists of a direct wave plus wave created by reflection from the ground. This action compares to mirror reflection and the laws of optics apply equally well to radio wave reflection. Reflected wave can be considered to come from an "image antenna" located as far below the earth's surface as the real antenna is above it. Strength of the reflected wave depends upon antenna height and the conductivity of the earth.

* * * * * *

broadcast band may be hundreds of miles under good conditions. Ground wave propagation in the hf spectrum, on the other hand, is limited to tens of miles, and is primarily limited to the horizon in the vhf spectrum. Long distance hf propagation takes place mainly because of wave reflection from the ionosphere, as discussed later in this chapter.

Fig. 3 shows a vertical antenna above a perfect, flat ground. At a distant point a wave received from this antenna consists of a direct wave plus the wave created by reflection from the ground in the vicinity of the antenna. At a more distant point, only the reflected wave is received. This action can be compared to mirror reflection and the laws of optics that govern mirrors apply equally well to radio wave reflection. In the general case, the angle of the incident wave from the antenna to the ground (a) equals the angle of the reflected wave (b), with a portion of the reflected wave being absorbed or refracted by the ground. The intensity of the combined waves at a distant point varies with respect to antenna height above ground, the angle of reflection, and also the reflective efficiency (electrical conductivity) of the ground. The vertical radiation pattern of the antenna is therefore determined by the sum of the direct wave from the antenna and the ground-reflected wave.

In the case of a horizontally polarized antenna (a dipole, for example), reflection from a perfect, flat ground gives a phase (polarity) shift for the reflected wave of 180 degrees at most angles above the horizon with little wave attenuation. Even over poor, low conductivity ground, the reflected wave retains nearly the same phase relationship to the direct wave and almost the same intensity, as ground absorption is low. Thus, the reflected wave patterns obtained over real-life ground closely resemble theoretical results determined mathematically.

Ground reflection produces quite different results in the case of the vertical antenna. There is little phase shift of the reflected wave at high reflection angles, but a considerable phase shift at lower reflection angles. As an example, for a very small reflection angle (b) when the vertical antenna is close to the ground, the phase shift of the reflected wave is nearly 180 degrees when ground absorption is small, just as in the case of the horizontal antenna. But as the reflection angle increases, the phase shift decreases until, at a critical "Brewster angle", phase shift drops to 90 degrees and wave attenuation is a maximum. This critical angle ranges from about 10 degrees above

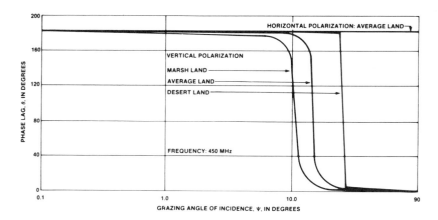

Fig. 4 Phase change of wave caused by ground reflection for vertical and horizontal polarizations. The phase stays virtually constant at 180 degrees for horizontal polarization and changes substantially for vertical polarization. Phase change takes place at an angle of reflection between 10 and 30 degrees depending upon soil conductivity. (Drawing courtesy of "Mobile Radio Technology" magazine.)

the horizon for good ground (a salt marsh,for example) to over 30 degrees for low conductivity (rocky, sandy) ground (Fig. 4). At this angle, the radiation pattern of a vertical antenna is affected the most by ground reflection.

Below the Brewster angle the reflected wave from a vertical antenna partially cancels the direct wave, while above this angle ground reflection enhances the direct wave, providing a gain up to 6 decibels over free-space conditions. This gain is theoretical, as no antenna in the vicinity of the earth is in free space.

In any case, the better the ground conductivity, the lower the critical angle and the greater the low-angle radiation from the vertical antenna. This may be the reason that such conflicting results are reported by amateurs using vertical antennas. Those amateurs living in areas of poor ground conductivity are bound to have poorer low-angle radiation from a

Fig. 5 Effective ground conductivity in the United States. The larger number indicates higher conductivity. Conductivity is expressed in millimhos per meter. (Drawing courtesy of "Reference Data for Radio Engineers".)

given vertical antenna than those amateurs lucky enough to reside in a region of very good ground conductivity. Fortunately, except for desert areas and regions with very rocky soil, most of the United States lies in an area having fair to good ground conductivity (Fig 5).

Ground Reflection Patterns for Vertical Antennas

Vertical polarization has important advantages over horizontal, especially when antenna space is limited. Fig. 6 compares the vertical field pattern of a horizontal dipole and a quarter-wave vertical antenna located above good ground. As an example, assume that for long distance communication a vertical radiation angle of 20 degrees or less is desired.

To achieve maximum radiation at this angle, it is necessary to place the horizontal antenna about

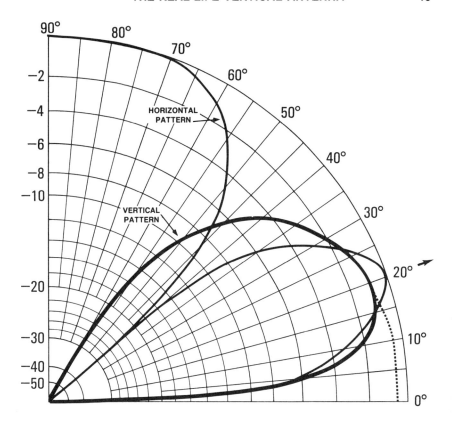

Fig. 6 A comparison of the vertical field patterns of horizontal and vertical antennas located above good ground. The horizontal antenna is 3/4-wavelength above ground while the base of vertical antenna is at ground level. Both antennas provide good radiation at a vertical angle of about 20 degrees but horizontal antenna must be 52 feet high to do the job on the 20 meter band.

3/4-wavelength above ground. The vertical antenna, however, radiates maximum power at or near this vertical angle when the base is at ground level. For the 20 meter band, this requires a horizontal antenna height of about 52 feet (15.8m) compared with an overall height of only 16.5 feet (5m) for the vertical antenna.

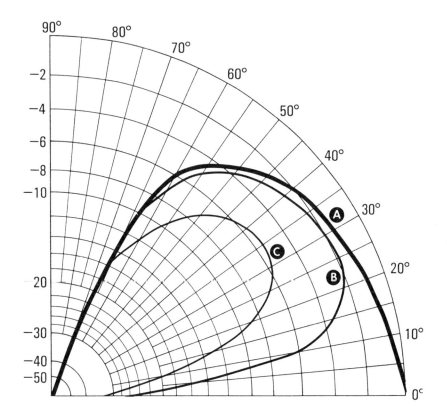

Fig. 7 Vertical radiation pattern of a vertical dipole whose base is at ground level. Over perfect ground, low angle radiation is maximum at the horizon (A). Over average ground (B), typical of the United States, some extremely low angle radiation is lost. Poor ground conductivity (C) reduces radiation at all vertical angles.

Theoretically, the vertical antenna provides a maximum radiation field down to zero degrees (the horizon), as shown by the dashed line. However, since the earth is not a perfect conductor, the extreme low angle radiation is not realizable.

Note that the very high angle radiation lobe of the horizontal antenna is useless for most long distance, high frequency communication. It is this high angle lobe, on the other hand, that makes this

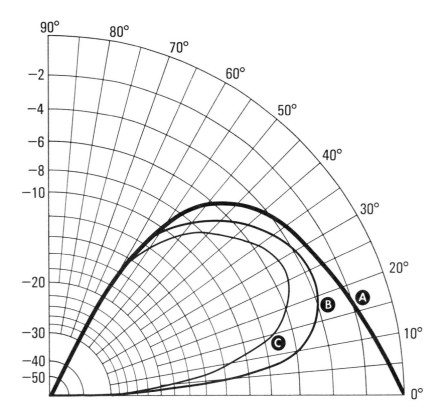

Fig. 8 Vertical radiation pattern of a ground plane antenna with the base at ground level resembles vertical dipole pattern, with ground absorption losses showing below about 15 degrees. A = perfect ground, B = average ground, C = poor ground.

antenna type outperform the vertical on short-haul communication on the lower frequency bands (160 and 80 meters, for example).

The elevation pattern of the vertical antenna at various heights above ground shows interesting low angle radiation. The pattern of a vertical dipole whose base is at ground level is shown in Fig. 7. Over perfect ground the low angle radiation is maximum at the horizon as shown by curve A. Over average ground (typical for the USA), some of the

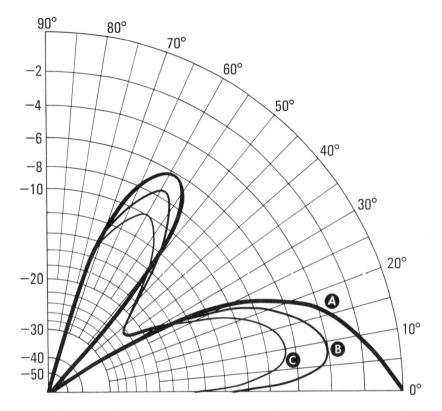

Fig. 9 Vertical radiation pattern of a ground plane antenna with the base elevated one-half wavelength above ground. Radiation is concentrated at a slightly lower angle than when antenna is ground mounted. Second, high-angle lobe appears at about 60 degrees above the horizon. A = perfect ground, B = average ground, C = poor ground.

extremely low angle radiation is lost but at an elevation angle of only 15 degrees, for example, the radiation lobe is down less than 3 dB in power from the maximum theoretical value (curve B). Poor ground conductivity, such as found in dry, semi-desert areas, further reduces low angle radiation, as shown in curve C.

The elevation pattern of a quarter-wave ground plane antenna with the base at ground level is shown in Fig. 8. The pattern is much the same as that of a

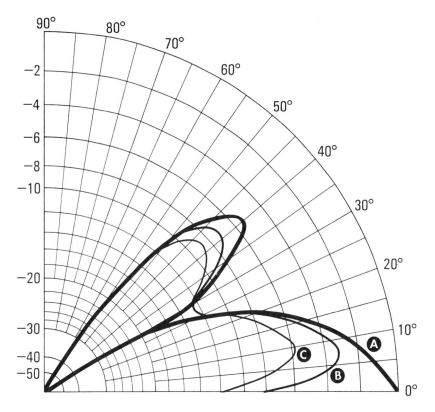

Fig. 10 Vertical radiation pattern of a ground plane antenna with the base elevated three-quarters wavelength above ground. High angle lobe drops to about 40 degrees. A = perfect ground, B = average ground, C = poor ground.

vertical half-wave dipole, with ground absorption loss showing at angles below about 15 degrees. In most typical installations radiation below 10 degrees is virtually zero.

The Elevated Vertical Antenna

Fig. 9 represents the pattern of a ground plane antenna with the base elevated one-half wavelength above the ground. Radiation is concentrated at a

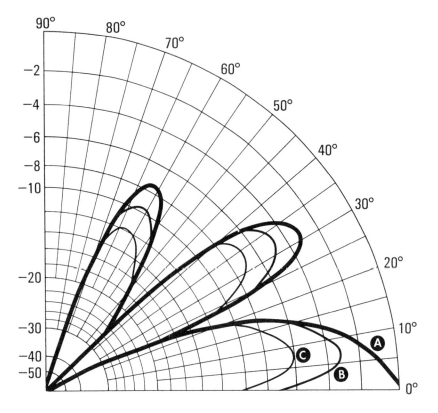

Fig. 11 Vertical radiation pattern of a ground plane antenna with the base elevated one wavelength above ground. Three main lobes are shown, with the lowest an an angle of less than 10 degrees above the horizon. A = perfect ground, B = average ground, C = poor ground.

slightly lower angle than when the antenna is ground mounted, and a second, high-angle radiation lobe appears at about 60 degrees above the horizon. This lobe is useful for high angle, hf multiple-hop propagation such as occasionally found on "long path" openings.

When the ground plane antenna is elevated so the base is three-quarters wavelength above ground (Fig. 10) the lower lobe radiation angle drops to about 8 degrees over average ground and the high angle lobe has split in two, providing maximum radiation at about 60 degrees and 30 degrees above the horizon.

Fig. 11 shows the vertical pattern of the ground plane at an elevation of one wavelength above ground. Three main lobes are shown, with the lowest at an angle of less than 10 degrees above the horizon. The two higher lobes are at angles of about 32 and 62 degrees.

Elevating the vertical antenna is impractical on the lower frequency bands because of the size of the antenna, but it can improve overall DX results on the higher frequency amateur bands, especially since boosting antenna height helps to raise the antenna with respect to nearby metallic objects and power lines.

As with any antenna, theoretical considerations are greatly modified in a practical environment but the vertical antenna stands on its own merits as a popular and effective hf transmitting antenna even though it is more susceptible to ground resistance loss than an equivalent horizontal antenna. Ground loss are covered in the next chapter.

Ionospheric Reflection

The vertical angle of wave reflection from an antenna in the vicinity of the ground is an important factor in long distance hf communication because the radio wave is reflected again in the ionosphere at a distant point and returned to earth. The angles of reflection determine the wave path.

For long distance communication, the optimum angle of ionospheric reflection depends upon the height of the ionosphere, the length of the path and seasonal factors (Fig. 12).

As an example, an ionospheric height of 350 km (210 mi) is shown in the drawing. Maximum distance of the first reflection point from ionosphere to ground is about 4160 km (2500 mi) from the transmitter. This corresponds to a vertical angle of

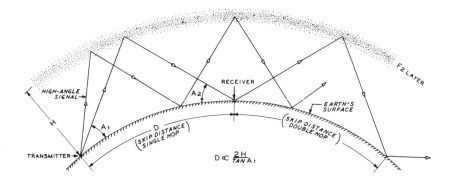

Fig. 12 Single-hop transmission takes place up to distances of about 2500 miles. This corresponds to a vertical angle of reflection at the antenna of zero degrees above the horizon. Multiple-hop transmission reaches distant points. Silent (skip) zones between the hop points are shown. Broad vertical angle of radiation of antenna covers much area between hop points. (Drawing courtesy of "Beam Antenna Handbook", Radio Publications, Inc.)

reflection above the horizon at the antenna of zero degrees. As the vertical angle of reflection increases, the distance to the first ionospheric reflection point decreases and the "skip distance" to the area where the signal returns to earth is decreased. The laws of reflection point out that for greatest DX work, the angle of ground wave reflection must be low in order to have the greatest single-hop transmission distance.

This does not imply that the transmitting antenna must direct its energy in a thin beam along the horizon to the distant ionosphere. This is not what happens in practical antennas. Rather, the vertical radiation pattern of an antenna is quite broad (20 to 40 degrees) and the energy is "sprayed" over a large area of the ionosphere. This insures that some portion of the energy comes back to earth at a distant point in spite of random variations in the ionosphere.

Generally speaking, even though the vertical antenna pattern is broad for a given long distance circuit and a given frequency, the lower the angle of radiation of the antenna the stronger will be the signal at a distant point.

Multiple-hop Reflection

For distances longer than 2500 miles (4160 km),several ionospheric reflections are normally required (Fig. 12). On a very long path (New York to Australia, for example), many reflections may take place. Unfortunately, the signal loss for each ionospheric "hop" can run as high as 6 dB due to wave absorption and scattering in the ionosphere and to ground absorption.Thus, to achieve the strongest signal at a distant point, the fewer the ionospheric hops the better.

Because of the geometry of reflection, as discussed earlier, a practical vertical antenna is theoretically able to provide greater low-angle reflected energy than an equivalent horizontal antenna limited to a reasonable height above ground. This is valid on all amateur hf bands, and particularly true on the 160 and 80 meter bands, where even an antenna a half-wavelength high is generally impractical.

Horizontal vs Vertical--Not a True Comparison

One other factor influences the performance of a vertical antenna when compared to a horizontal equivalent. While the horizontal antenna can provide attractive low angle radiation over rather poor conductivity ground, it may prove impossible to erect the antenna high enough in the air to take advantage of the resulting low angle radiation. As a practical example, consider a horizontal antenna mounted 35 feet (10.7 m) above ground for 40 meter operation. This corresponds to an electrical height of one-quarter wavelength. Maximum radiation in the vertical plane from this antenna is at 90 degrees to the horizon (straight up) and radiation at a DX-angle of 10 degrees is reduced about 12 dB below the maximum field.

In comparison, a vertical quarter-wave antenna with the base at ground level provides a degree of radiation at a vertical angle of 10 degrees above the horizon. If ground conductivity is average, the field strength at this vertical angle is 6 dB below the maximum theoretical value. It seems as if both antennas suffer a handicap in reduced field strength at a low DX-angle of radiation.

Are the handicaps equal? The vertical field patterns indicate the vertical antenna is about 6 dB better than the horizontal at a 10 degree vertical angle. But this comparison may be misleading. It is like comparing apples and oranges.

Amateurs who are fortunate to have two antennas in this physical arrangement on the 40 meter band conclude that the antennas are roughly equal in performance when they are located over average ground. That is, a dipole about 35 feet in the air compares favorably in transmission and reception at 40 meters with a ground mounted quarter-wave ground plane antenna. In some instances one or the other antennas seem to favor a particular propagation path, but the advantage is a small one and not consistent, with one exception: the horizontal antenna always provides a stronger signal for short distance communication. That is, the high angle radiation of the horizontal provides much stronger signals for close-in work than does the vertical. But over about 700 miles (1160 km) on the 40 meter band, the two antennas seem equal. The same results hold true on 80 meters, except the area of signal equality lies much closer to the antenna (about 500 miles, or 830 km).

The comparison is even more striking on the 160 meter band. It is nearly impossible to erect a horizontal antenna one quarter wavelength high on this band and most amateurs are content with an antenna height of 60 feet (18 m) or less. This corresponds to an electrical height of about one-eighth wavelength and at this elevation low angle radiation from a horizontal antenna is almost nil.

Because it is difficult to achieve low-angle radiation from a low horizontal antenna, the preferred DX antenna of many operators on the 160 and 80 meter bands is the vertical --even a short one having low overall efficiency. A horizontal antenna is satisfactory for local, around-the-state communication on the low bands and many amateurs have worked DX with just such an antenna, but it is considered to be a poor DX performer by those who have taken the time and effort to erect a good vertical antenna system.

As a practical example, one of the authors of this handbook compared a horizontal dipole 40 feet (12 m) high against a short, coil-loaded ground plane 40 feet high whose base was mounted 8 feet (2.4 m) above the ground. A network of six radials was used with the ground plane antenna (Fig. 13). Tests were run on 80 meters for more than three years and the results were quite consistent. Out to about 600 miles (1000 km) the low dipole provided the superior signal, often by 10 to 30 decibels, as compared to the ground plane. At a distance of about 1200 miles (2000 km) signal reports were usually the same for both antennas. But at greater distances the vertical antenna consistently proved to be the better performer. Transoceanic contacts could be easily worked with the vertical; often the DX signals could not be heard on the horizontal. DX signal reports received on the horizontal proved to be 10 to 15 dB weaker than those received on the vertical. Clearly, except for local work, the vertical antenna was the star DX performer on 80 meters!

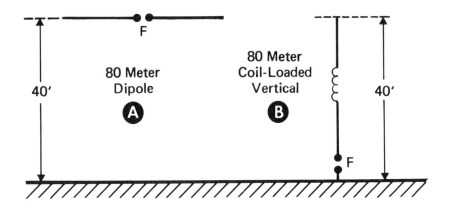

Fig. 13 Comparative tests were run on 80 meter dipole and ground plane antennas. Low dipole proved best up to about 600 miles distance. Both antennas seemed about equal at 1200 miles distance. For long distance work, the ground plane antenna was the better performer.

The Picture Changes Above 7 MHz

While the vertical antenna proves to be the superior antenna for low-band DX, the picture changes at 7 MHz and above. Now it is possible to erect a horizontal antenna high in the air in terms of operating wavelength. A comparison of a 40 foot (12 m) high dipole and a ground-mounted, full-size ground plane at 7 MHz showed the former better for close-in work, but the two antennas seemed about equal for DX operation. The vertical antenna was better for very long contacts (California to Saudi-Arabia, for example) and the improvement was consistent, but it was not of great magnitude.

The final comparisions between simple horizontal and vertical antennas took place on the 10, 15 and 20 meter bands. In each test the horizontal antenna was 40 feet (12 m) high and the base of the ground plane antenna was 8 feet (2.4 m) above ground. Six radials were used on each vertical ground plane antenna.

These arrangements were chosen because they are typical of an "average" amateur installation. Tests were run on worldwide and domestic contacts for a period of over two years. Signal reports showed that the horizontal dipole had about 6 dB (approximately one S-unit) advantage over the ground plane most of the time on long propagation paths on all bands. The improvement was most noticeable on the 15 and 10 meter bands where dipole height was large in terms of wavelength.

On quite a few occasions the vertical antenna outperformed the dipole on DX contacts by as much as an S-unit. Greatest improvement was noticed during disturbed ionospheric conditions. During excellent DX conditions, the dipole proved to be the better antenna. Even so, plenty of flattering reports were received on the vertical antenna. After all, if you are S9-plus 20 dB on one antenna, does it matter if you are only S9-plus 15 dB on another antenna?

Many similar tests have been run by the authors over a 35 year period and have been repeated several times in different locations. Other amateurs have also contributed to the tests. While the high dipole proves to be the better performer on the higher bands a majority of the time, the ionosphere is a great leveler of signals. On all bands (except 10 and possibly 15 meters), the slight loss of signal strength for the ground plane antenna may be of no consequence, considering the savings in space and the unobtrusiveness of the installation as compared to a dipole antenna.

But the last word has not been said about the vertical antenna, as explained in the next section.

The High Vertical Antenna

It is easy to raise the vertical antenna above ground in terms of operating wavelength on the higher frequencies. Getting any type of antenna high in the air is the secret to success on any amateur band. While the theoretical vertical radiation pattern of a vertical antenna mounted a distance above the ground shows some high angle radiation, the antenna is still an effective low-angle DX radiator. It disproves the old saying that "the vertical antenna is equally weak in all directions". One reason for the improved performance is that a high antenna can be placed in the clear as far as local obstructions are concerned.

The Japan-California Tests

In the late 1950s extended tests were run between California and a Marine Corps amateur station located in Japan. The 20 and 10 meter bands were used and tests were run for over a year. The station in Japan had three element Yagi beams about 40 feet high (12.2 m) and ground plane antennas atop masts nearly 90 feet (27.4 m) high.

On both bands, results on the Japan-California path were interesting. Under good conditions, the beams were about one S-unit (6 dB) louder than the corresponding ground plane. Under poor conditions, or when the band was just opening in the morning or closing in the evening, the ground planes were the superior antennas, providing stronger signals with less fading.

Encouraged by the results, the Marine Corps hams moved the ground plane antennas to the top of a 200 foot (61 m) high chimney. The results over a long period of time showed that the ground plane antennas were nearly the equal of the 40 foot high Yagi beams and in many circumstances provided superior signals. Unfortunately, the tests were broken off when the operators in Japan returned stateside and the ham station was closed down.

Not many amateurs can place their antenna on a 200 foot chimney, but an amateur living in an apartment building can obtain excellent results from a simple ground plane antenna mounted on the roof. And an amateur living in a multistory dwelling should certainly investigate the idea of placing a vertical antenna on the roof if open yard space is scarce!

Jumping to Conclusions About Vertical Antennas

It is not easy to reach specific conclusions from a series of unrelated tests performed at random over many years. But the fact remains that the vertical antenna is a good DX performer under difficult conditions and, when installed with care, provides good results. The best possible world is to have both horizontal and vertical antennas yourself and make comparisons that are meaningful to you.

There is no simple answer to the choice between the antennas. A lot depends upon the band you use, the results desired, and the amount of real estate you have available. Surely on the 160 and 80 meter bands the serious operator will choose the vertical, as it is a star DX performer and there is no real competition to it. However, if you enjoy local rag chews on these bands and are not an all-night DX chaser, a horizontal antenna about 40 feet (12 m) in the air will do a good job for you. If it is higher, the results will be better, but don't expect such an antenna to win a DX contest for you!

The Favorite Antennas of W6SAI

"My favorite antenna for 160 or 80 meters is a dipole because I don't chase DX on these bands. I like to rag-chew. Besides, the vertical antenna is sensitive to noise, and most noise is vertically polarized. I have a very high noise level and I have trouble hearing weak signals on a vertical. I can work some DX on the dipoles (east coast on 160 meters and Europe on 80 meters) but I know my old ground planes in my previous location were much better DX performers on these bands.

"On the 40 and 30 meter bands, the situation is a toss-up. My power line noise is much less on these bands and the vertical antennas do a good job on transmission and reception. On the whole, I'll chose the verticals for these bands. In any event, I can't compete with the 40 meter Yagis that are showing up but I can give a DX good acount of myself with the vertical.

"On the higher bands (20 through 10 meters) it is easy for me to erect a dipole 50 feet (15 m) in the air. The horizontal antenna is my choice beacuse it is easy to install and provides excellent results. I have ground planes for these bands, too, from time to time. They are located about 12 feet (3.6 m)above ground. But the radials are inconvenient, running around the yard, so they don't stay up except for occasional tests. I've made WAC (Worked All Continents) and DXCC with the verticals and 150 watts power, so you can say they work fine for me. In the long run, however, I'd choose a six element Yagi on a 150 foot (46 m) high tower any day! Since I don't have the room, time or money to erect such a giant, I have a lot of fun with the simple antennas that I have!"

The Favorite Antennas of W2LX

" I lived in an area that had good soil conductivity, near Long Island Sound (NY). I had a Yagi at 45 feet and several ground plane antennas at a base height of 10.5 feet (3.2 m). The Yagi beam outperformed the ground planes, but the ground planes were equal in every respect to single band dipoles that I tried from time to time. And they were a lot easier to maintain in bad weather than was the beam.

" I ran many skeds with Australia using the ground plane on 14 MHz and worked plenty of DX with this simple antenna--even with my QRP 4-watt rig. A few months before I moved, I took down the tower and the Yagi beam and just used the ground plane. I hate to admit it, but for my style of operating, I really didn't miss the beam.

"Now I am living in an area where it is difficult to erect a beam antenna. So I am using ground plane antennas and am satisfied. I may not be the loudest signal on the band, but I work plenty of DX and can compete in the pile-ups. My advice is not to envy the boys with the big antennas. A good operator with a simple antenna can even the score more times than you would imagine!"

The Choice: Horizontal Versus Vertical Antenna

The choice is interesting and in most case is dictated by the space available and monetary considerations. Consider these virtues of the vertical antenna:

1. A vertical antenna is inexpensive and simple to build and install. It occupies little ground space.

2. A vertical antenna can be conveniently fed at the base by a coaxial line and a simple matching network.

3. A vertical antenna is unobtrusive and draws little attention from curious neighbors.

4. A vertical antenna is nondirectional and does not require a rotator.

5. Low angle radiation can be obtained from the vertical antenna in the lower frequency ham bands where practical horizontal antenna heights provide only high angle radiation.

6. A multiband vertical antenna is inexpensive compared to the cost of a multiband beam.

Now consider the case for the horizontal antenna:

1. The horizontal antenna is less susceptible to man-made interference (auto ignition,power line noise, etc.) than is the vertical antenna.

2. The horizontal antenna is less affected by ground resistance in the near-area of the antenna than is the vertical.

3. Since many tv and fm antenna lead-in wires run in the vertical plane, a nearby vertical transmitting antenna may cause more TVI overload to a nearby receiver than would an equivalent horizontal antenna. The leadin of the entertainment equipment can act as an antenna, picking up signals radiated by the vertical transmitting antenna. (On the other side of the coin, many horizontal antennas are badly affected by noise in nearby power lines running parallel to the antenna.)

4. No extensive ground system is required for the horizontal antenna, whereas an extensive one may be required for good vertical antenna performance.

Can the "Fellow at the Other End" Tell the Difference?

Variations in transmitter power, antenna gain and angle of radiation can be observed at a distant receiving point, but it is unlikely that the casual listener can identify anything but major changes in these parameters without accurate instruments. Real-life propagation conditions tend to blur changes in transmission parameters that are readily predictable on paper. The majority of amateur contacts are of a random nature and if propagation does not support communication in one direction, it will support it in another.

Amateurs find to their dismay that they are hemmed in by neighbors, power lines, tv antennas, building codes, and financial considerations that limit the antenna of their choice. In these cases, and others, the worth of the vertical antenna system conclusively proves itself.

The VHF Vertical Antenna

So far no mention has been made of the use of the vertical antenna on the 6 meter band and the higher vhf bands. Antenna polarization plays a different role here as there is little if any ionospheric reflection on these bands (except possibly on 6 meters at the peak of the sunspot cycle).

Vertical polarization is very popular on the vhf bands, principally because a lot of mobile operation takes place here, and it is easy to mount a small vertical antenna on a vehicle. Most fm repeaters are vertically polarized; however, some of the DX and sideband operators choose horizontal polarization. They have no interest in repeaters and it is easier to build large horizontally polarized arrays than the vertical equivalents. Many vhf operators have both antenna polarizations available and use one or the other depending upon the type of operating they are doing.

The conclusion is that vhf antenna polarization is chosen to meet practical operating needs and not because one type of polarization is better than another. And this common-sense conclusion can apply equally well to the hf region!

Scaling Antenna Designs

It may be desired to build an antenna to operate at some frequency removed from an amateur band. The designs shown in this handbook can be scaled to another frequency by the following ratio: The new dimension equals the original dimension multiplied by the original frequency in MHz. The product is then divided by the new frequency in MHz.

For example, assume a 14.15 MHz half-wave element measures 33.07 feet (10.08 m) long. What will be its new length when scaled to 10.1 MHz?

The new dimension is equal to 33.07 times 14.15 divided by 10.1, or 46.33 feet (14.12 m).

More About HF Propagation

High frequency propagation is too complex a subject to cover completely in this handbook. For those interested in learning more about the subject, the following publications are recommended:

Jacobs and Cohen, "The Shortwave Propagation Handbook", 2d edition, CQ Book Shop, 76 North Broadway, Hicksville, NY 11801.

Hall, Woodward and DeMaw, "The ARRL Antenna Book", 14th edition, American Radio Relay League, Newington, CT 06111.

Computerized Propagation Programs

Computerized propagation programs have been used for some years by the Voice of America, the British Broadcasting Corporation and others involved in shortwave radio communication.

A version of a program developed by the U.S. Navy has been adapted for use on home computers and is available under such names as "Miniplot" or "MUFplot". The MUFplot program was derived from measurements made over a complete sunspot cycle from over 4700 test sites on 23 different paths that circled the globe. The results obtained from this, and other programs, compare favorably to preductions made by larger computer systems and to actual MUF observations.

Chapter 2

The Radio Ground

An electrical ground is a common reference point in a circuit which is at the same potential as the earth. Earth is literally taken as "ground", but not all earth provides a good ground, as discussed in this chapter.

The radio (rf) ground is a reference point in any circuit at which rf voltage is taken as zero. Radio and electrical grounds are the same in most circuits, but they can be quite different. If the resistance (or impedance, to use a fancy term) between radio and electric grounds is very low, they may be assumed to be the same.

The Electrical Ground

In house wiring the electrical ground is the equipment ground to which all exposed metallic surfaces are connected to reduce shock hazard. Most modern home wiring in the USA is a single phase, three wire system having one neutral wire (white), one "hot" wire (black, blue, or red) and an equipment (electric) ground wire (green or bare copper), as depicted in Fig. 1. The neutral and equipment ground conductors are grounded to earth at, or near, the distribution transformer or fuse block of the residence.

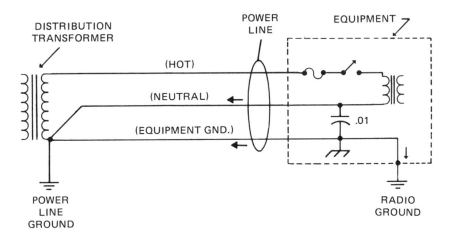

Fig. 1 RF ground currents reach earth via the equipment power line as well as by the radio ground (arrows). For best radio results, the rf and power line grounds should be decoupled by placing an rf choke in the power line (see text).

Separating the Radio (rf) and Electrical Grounds

Figure 1 shows that two radio ground paths exist in the circuit-- the intentional radio ground at the equipment and also the electrical ground at the distribution transformer. The later serves as a radio ground, whether the operator desires it or not, as rf ground currents from the antenna circuit can return to earth via both of the paths. The unwanted path through the power cable is closely coupled to the "hot" conductor and feeds some rf energy into the house wiring. This can result in unwanted TVI and RFI in nearby home entertainment equipment.

The radio and equipment grounds can be separated allowing each to do its specific task by decoupling the power cord to the transmitter through an rf choke (Fig. 2). The power cord is simply wrapped around a toroid or ferrite rod.This prevents rf

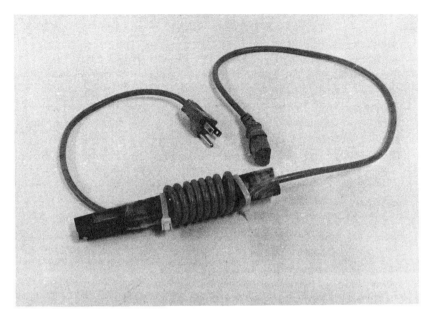

Fig. 2 Wrapping the power cord to the transmitting equipment around a ferrite core or rod decouples it from the power line ground, This helps to prevent rf currents from passing down the power cord instead of going to earth via the radio ground connection at the transmitter.

currents from passing down the power line instead of going to earth via the radio ground connection at the transmitter.

Ground Conductivity and Resistivity

Since the days of Marconi, transmitter engineers have been concerned with rf power lost in the ground. Early broadcasters made exhaustive studies of ground loss. An early description of this phenomenon was given by G.H. Brown in his classic "Proceedings of the IRE" article of February, 1935: "In the operation of the usual transmitting antenna, the conduction current in the antenna diminishes as we proceed upward along the antenna. This is explained by displacement currents which are assumed to flow in the antenna, through space, to the conducting plane below. This conducting plane completes the circuit by forming the return path to the base of the antenna. If this plane is not a perfect conductor, some power must be expended in returning the current to the base of the antenna."

A few months later, Brown expanded his view of the role played by the ground in radio transmission. "Ground systems below an antenna play a dual role. One function of the ground system is to provide a good conducting path for earth currents, so that these currents will not flow through a poorly conducting earth. The other function is to act as a good reflector for radio waves coming from the antenna, so that the vertical radiation pattern will be close to that obtained if the earth under the antenna were perfectly conducting".

Today, radio engineers have a good concept of the role played by the ground in the transmission of radio waves. A radio wave striking the ground is partially absorbed, causing currents to flow in the earth which are attenuated with distance at a rate determined by ground conductivity, frequency, angle of incidence and wave polarization. Depth of penetration of the wave is about 5 to 10 feet (1.5 to 3 m) for 75 percent current attenuation in the hf region. Thus, ground currents for a particular antenna are affected by antenna position and by conditions existing on and beneath the earth's surface for a considerable distance around the antenna.

Good conductivity (low resistivity) exists in moist, flat, rich soil and marshy ground. Poorer conductivity is found in pastoral land and forested areas. The latter soil is found in much of the USA and is termed "average ground". Poorer conductivity is found in heavy clay soil and rocky, sandy earth typical of coastal country. Needless to say, the worst ground conductivity is found in built-up industrial areas (Table 1).

SOIL	RESISTIVITY OHM-CM		
	AVERAGE	MIN.	MAX.
Fills—ashes, cinders, brine wastes	2,370	590	7,000
Clay, shale, gumbo, loam	4,060	340	16,300
Same—with varying proportions of sand and gravel	15,800	1,020	135,000
Gravel, sand, stones, with little clay or loam	94,000	59,000	458,000

SOIL	RESISTIVITY, OHM-CM (RANGE)		
Surface soils, loam, etc.	100	—	5,000
Clay	200	—	10,000
Sand and gravel	5,000	—	100,000
Surface limestone	10,000	—	1,000,000
Limestones	500	—	400,000
Shales	500	—	10,000
Sandstone	2,000	—	200,000
Granites, basalts, etc.		100,000	
Decomposed gneisses	5,000	—	50,000
Slates, etc.	1,000	—	10,000

Table 1. Resistivities of different soils. (U.S. Bureau of Standards Technical Report 108.)

In all cases, ground resistivity is lower in the rainy seasons than in dry weather as ground water dissolves the salts in the earth and increases conductivity near the surface.

For the case of the vertical antenna, ground loss is important because the electric field of the wave cuts through the earth's surface inducing ground currents which must travel through the lossy ground back to the antenna. As a result, there is a dissipation of energy that represents power lost from the radio wave.

In addition to power loss in the soil, ground resistivity up to a distance of about 10 wavelengths

| MOISTURE CONTENT, | RESISTIVITY, OHM-CM | |
% BY WEIGHT	TOP SOIL	SANDY LOAM
0	$1,000 \times 10^6$	$1,000 \times 10^6$
2.5	250,000	150,000
5	165,000	43,000
10	53,000	18,500
15	1,000	10,500
20	12,000	6,300
30	6,400	4,200

ADDED SALT % BY WEIGHT OF MOISTURE	RESISTIVITY, OHM-CM
0	10,700
0.1	1,800
1.0	460
5	190
10	130
20	100

* For sandy loam—moisture content, 15% by weight; temperature, 17°C (63°F).

Table 2. Earth resistance depends upon type of soil, the amount of moisture, and the salt content. Naturally occuring salts in the earth dissolved in ground water lower resistivity.

from the antenna affects the low angle radiation of the vertical antenna as discussed in the previous chapter.

What Affects Ground Conductivity?

Ground conductivity (or resistivity) depends to a large extent upon the type of soil, the amount of moisture in it, and the salt content. Moisture varies with the season of the year, the amount of rain, and the depth of the natural water table. When very dry, most all soils have high electrical resistivity and poor conductivity, but even with a

| TEMPERATURE | | RESISTIVITY, OHM-CM |
C	F	
20	68	7,200
10	50	9,900
0	32 (water)	13,800
0	32 (ice)	30,000
− 5	23	79,000
−15	14	330,000

*For sandy loam, 15.2% moisture.

Table 3. Earth resistance is dependent upon temperature. When soil and water freeze, conductivity drops and resistivity increases rapidly.

slight moisture content soil resistivity drops rapidly. Naturally occuring salts in the earth dissolved in ground water lower resistivity, as summarized in Table 2.

In addition to the moisture content, soil conductivity is dependent upon temperature. When soil and water freeze, conductivity drops appreciably and resistivity increases rapidly as soil temperature drops below freezing. Because of these effects, soil conductivity varies considerably with the seasons of the year, particularly in locations where there are extremes of temperature (Table 3).

In the main, ground conductivity, aside from the small area directly below the antenna, is uncontrollable because the total area of signal reflection is large around a typical antenna. The fact remains, however, that vertical antenna performace is more sensitive to the degree of ground conductivity than is an equivalent horizontal antenna.

In addition to losses caused by induced ground currents, ground resistance is of interest because it is in series with the radition resistance of the antenna and transmitter power is divided between the two resistances. That power flowing through ground

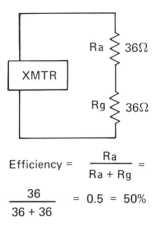

$$\text{Efficiency} = \frac{Ra}{Ra + Rg} =$$

$$\frac{36}{36 + 36} = 0.5 = 50\%$$

Fig. 3 Ground resistance (Rg) is in series with feedpoint resistance (Ra). In a Marconi antenna efficiency requires low ground resistance. In this example, ground resistance is equal to the antenna feedpoint resistance and overall antenna effiency is fifty percent.

resistance is lost so it is important to do eveything possible to make ground resistance low with respect to radiation resistance, as discussed in the next section.

Radiation and Feedpoint Resistance

All antennas exhibit a quality called radiation resistance. It is described as that value of resistance which, when substituted for the resonant antenna, will dissipate the same amount of power as is radiated by the antenna. The actual value of radiation resistance of a particular antenna is determined by the antenna configuration and its placement with respect to the earth and nearby objects. The quarter-wave ground plane, for example, has a radiation resistance of about 36 ohms, and short, coil-loaded vertical antennas show radiation resistance values in the range of 0.5 to 30 ohms. As stated earlier, radiation resistance is in series with ground resistance in an antenna cicuit and a

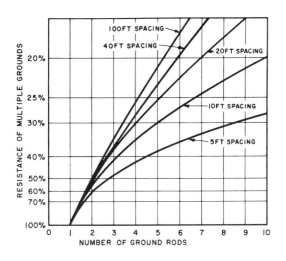

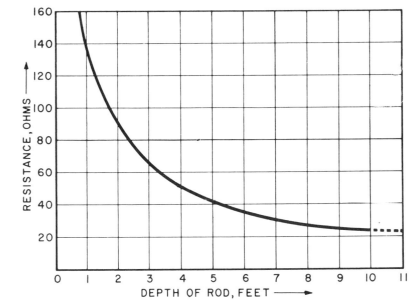

Fig. 4 Ground resistance decreases with depth of ground rod in earth. It is an exceptional ground connection that has a resistance of less than 20 ohms. ("Ground Connections for Electrical Systems", Peters, U. S. National Standards Technical Paper 108, Courtesy "CQ" magazine).

high ratio of radiation resistance to ground resistance results in an efficient antenna. If the antenna is resonant, the radiation resistance is termed "feedpoint resistance".

Ground Resistance and Antenna Efficiency

Ground resistance includes resistance of the ground itself and the resistance and reactance of the conductor connecting the radio equipment to ground. For example, if the radiation resistance of a Marconi antenna is 36 ohms (Ra) and the ground resistance (Rg) is also 36 ohms, overall antenna efficiency is equal to the radiation resistance divided by the sum of the resistances, as shown in Fig. 3. Overall antenna efficiency is 50 percent, which means that half the transmitter output power is wasted in ground resistance.

Values of ground resistance have been measured as high as 200 ohms in very poor soil, and it is an exceptional ground connection that has less than 20 ohms resistance (Fig. 4). Even at this low figure, overall efficiency of the example antenna drops to 64 percent. And if an antenna has a radiation resistance of only an ohm or two (as may be the case with a short, coil-loaded antenna), efficiency drops to only a few percent! It is clear that low ground resistance is important where antenna efficiency is concerned and this chapter tells you how to obtain a good , low-loss ground.

The Ground Connection

A simple means of making a radio ground connection is to drive a metal rod into the earth and to connect the radio equipment to it. A single ground rod, even if driven into soil of good conductivity, will not produce a low-loss ground cnnection as it does not contact enough of the soil.

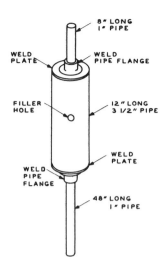

Fig. 5 Concrete-filled drive pipe makes job of driving ground rod easier. Butt end of ground rod is slipped into drive pipe and upper end of rod is driven downwards with the driver. When the drive pipe cylinder approaches ground level the driver is reversed and short section used as the drive. (Drawing courtesy of "Interference Handbook", Radio Publications, Inc.)

Multiple ground rods connected in parallel will do a better job.

A practical ground rod, readily available at electrical supply stores, is the Hubbard 9618 which is 3/8-inch (0.83 cm) diameter and 8 feet (2.44 m) long. The rod is steel core for easy driving and copper coated for good electrical conductivity. The rod is driven into the ground until only the top clears the soil. A single rod, driven into soil of good conductivity, will provide a radio ground having a resistance of about 20 to 30 ohms. Two ground rods spaced about 5 feet (1.5 m) apart and connected together with a heavy copper strap will drop the ground resistance by half.

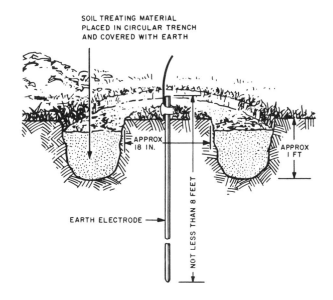

Fig. 6 The trench method of chemical soil treatment for ground rod. ("Practical Grounding Principles and Practices for Securing Safe, Dependable Grounds". Copperweld Corp., Glassport, PA).

The Ground Rod Driver

If the job is done right, it is not difficult to drive a ground rod into the soil. A steel post driver (available at a tool rental service) can be used, or the ground rod driver shown in Fig. 5 can be made up. The driver consists of a concrete filled steel cylinder with a driving pipe on one end and a guide pipe on the other.

To start the job, a hole about a foot (0.3 m) deep is dug at the location for the ground rod. The top end of the rod is slipped into the long section of the driver. This prevents the rod from buckling when the going gets difficult. The rod is centered in the hole and driving is started. Soaking the earth with water makes the job easier. A small ladder is required at first to allow the operator to deliver a sound blow with the driver. Using six inch blows, the rod penetration into the earth is started. Once a foot or two of the rod has entered the ground, longer strokes can be used. Continue this until the rod is as far into the ground as it will go using the long (guide) section of the driver.

At this point, the driver is reversed and the short section is slipped over the ground rod. Continue driving until the top of the rod is just above ground level. If multiple rods are used, connect them together with heavy wire or strap.

Some amateurs dig up the soil before the ground rod is driven and mix rock salt and gypsum (60-40 proportion) into the soil, which is then watered and tamped down. Treated soil is corrosive and should not touch the ground rod, so treatment is usually confined to a circular trench about the rod (Fig. 6).

Chemical treatment is not a permanent cure for high ground resistance as the chemicals are washed or leached away by rainfall and natural drainage through the soil. Care should be taken with this form of treatment as it may seriously pollute ground water. If the house gets water from a nearby well, the effect of pollution should certainly be investigated. Chemical treatment has the advantage of reducing seasonal variation in soil resistance that results from rainfall and runoff (Fig. 7).

Use the Home Plumbing System as a Ground?

Many residences are plumbed with copper water pipe that is soldered at the joints. This comprises a large area of metal in proximity to the ground and which is grounded at some point along its length. A ground connection to a cold water pipe has worked well for many amateurs trying to obtain an easy and inexpensive ground.

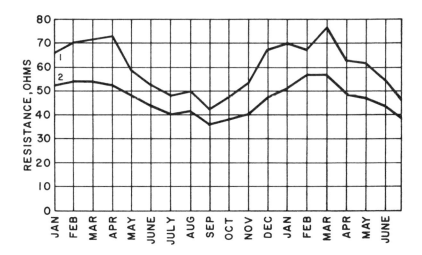

Fig. 7 Seasonal variation of earth resistance with 3/4-inch pipe driven in stony, clay soil. Depth of electrode in earth is 3 feet for curve 1, and 10 feet for curve 2.

At W6SAI a satisfactory radio ground for 160 and 80 meter operation is made to a convenient copper cold water pipe, the house plumbing then being connected to ground rods at each end of the residence.

If you are fortunate enough to have a yard sprinkling system consisting of copper pipe and soldered fittings, it will serve as an excellent ground, within the limits imposed by soil conductivity. Iron water pipe in the ground or in the house makes a poor ground connection because of the glue-like insulating material smeared on the joints before the pipes are connected.

Length of the Ground Connection Wire

An effective electrical ground can be ruined as a radio ground by an overly long ground connection wire. A rough rule-of-thumb for an effective radio ground wire length is that the length in feet should not be longer than one-tenth the operating frequency in meters. For example, a ground wire for 160 meter operation may be up to 16 feet long, but a ground wire for 20 meters should be less than 2 feet long! This imposes a major restriction on the user as it is impossible to achieve short ground leads in most amateur installations.

The necessity for a short ground lead is brought about by the fact that any wire has reactance (resistance to the flow of radio energy). Wire reactance can be reduced by shortening the wire, and using a wire having a large diameter. If the radio ground lead reactance is too high, the wire acts as a high impedance circuit, isolating the equipment from true ground!

The situation is even worse if the station equipment is located on the second, or higher, floor of a building. How is a good radio ground obtained in this case?

The solution to the problem is to place the ground connection at the antenna site instead of at the station. Either a direct ground connection or an artificial electrical ground can be used at the feedpoint of the antenna. All that is required at the station is an electrical ground for shock prevention. This connection can be made to the ground wire of the electrical system, or to a copper cold water pipe. Other ground connections are discussed later in this chapter.

The Series-tuned Ground Lead

An effective technique to electrically place a far away ground point directly at the radio equipment is to use a series-tuned ground lead (Fig.8). This circuit, when properly adjusted, reduces electrical ground lead length to virtually zero. An inductor and variable capacitor are placed in series with the ground lead at the equipment. The

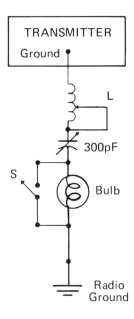

Fig. 8 The series-tuned ground lead. Inductor and variable capacitor are connected in series and tuned for maximum ground current during transmitter operation. Preliminary adjustment can be made with equipment off and dip oscillator coupled to coil. Capacitor and inductor are adjusted for resonance indication at operating frequency. Indicator bulb is shorted out after adjustments are completed.

capacitor is adjusted to provide series resonance of the ground lead at the operating frequency. Resonance is now established by placing an rf thermocouple ammeter in the ground lead and adjusting the capacitor for maximum ground current during transmission. If a thermocouple meter is unobtainable, a 6.2 volt, 3.9 ampere lamp (Chicago 1133, or equivalent) will do the job for a medium power transmitter. Once resonance has been established, the bulb (or meter) is shorted out.

The ground circuit is tuned to the operating frequency and if this is varied, the circuit will have to be retuned. If operation on several bands is desired, a tapped coil must be used to allow circuit flexibility.

This technique is especially effective if the antenna terminates at the transmitter, as in the case of the Marconi, and the radio ground connection must be made at that point.

The Artificial Radio Ground (Radial Ground Wire)

The radial ground wire (sometimes called a counterpoise) is a simple artifical rf ground that is very effective at placing the radio equipment at, or near, actual earth ground potential. It may be used alone, or in conjunction with another ground connection. Sometimes on the higher frequency bands (10 or 15 meters, for example) it is difficult to get a good ground and the operator finds the transmitting equipment is "hot". He may even get "bitten" by rf that appears on the microphone! The radial ground wire will cure this annoying problem.

In its simplest form, the radial ground is an insulated wire a quarter-wavelength long at the operating frequency. One end is connected to the ground terminal of the transmitter and the opposite end is left free. The wire is led away from the transmitter in a random direction, either outdoors or indoors (Fig. 9). The far end of the wire is taped to prevent contact, as it may be "hot" with rf energy and could cause a rf burn to anyone unfortunate enough to touch it while the transmitter is operating.

As the radial ground wire is resonant, it functions only on the band for which it is cut. However, several radial wires cut to different bands may be attached to the transmitter ground terminal for multiband operation.

Placement of the radial wire is not critical. It is usually run in the horizontal plane, along the floor of the radio room tacked against the wall, or

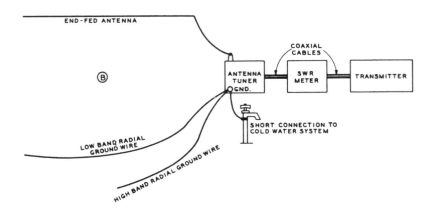

Fig. 9 Operation of Marconi or any end-fed antenna is improved when a radial ground wire is used along with a ground connection. A single radial wire is needed for each band of operation. Wire is cut to quarter-wave resonance. (Radial length for 160 meters is 132 feet; for 80 meters, 65 feet and for 40 meters, 33.5 feet.) Drawing courtesy of "Wire Antennas", Radio Publications, Inc.)

perhaps out the window and along the wall of the house. For the lower frequency bands, where the wire is quite long, it can be run through bushes and around the yard, a few inches above the ground.

The Ground Radial System

An outgrowth of the radial wire is a ground radial system composed of a number of wires run radially out from the transmitter or the antenna site. The wires may be buried a few inches in the ground, or run above the ground surface. Broadcast stations, which pay dearly to obtain the best possible ground system, generally run out 120 wires, each a quarter wavelength long, from the base of the antenna; the radials are spaced radially 3 degrees apart. When properly installed, this provides a ground system with a resistance of 1 ohm, or less.

Such a comprehensive ground system is beyond the pocketbook of most amateurs, but the idea is a sound one. It must be emphasized, however, that ground losses decrease as the number and length of radials increase. Experiments have indicated that a ground radial system consisting of 50 above-ground radials, 0.2 wavelength long, fanning out from the antenna base, provides a good ground system with an average resistance of under 5 ohms. A more modest installation consisting of about 15 radials, 0.1 wavelength long, has higher resistance but has worked well for many amateurs. Such a system, when tied in parallel with one or more ground rods, is an inexpensive, easily installed ground. The radials can be laid atop the ground, or buried a few inches by slitting the soil with a "Ditch Witch" trencher, available on a rental basis from many home improvement centers. Burying the radials does not improve the efficiency of the system, it merely prevents people from tripping over the wires.

To combat corrosion caused by acidic ground water, neoprene covered aluminum wire is recommended for buried radials.

The Ground Screen

Experiments conducted by Arch Doty, Jr. (K8CFU), John Frey (W3ESU), and Harry Mills (K4HU) described in the 1983 bulletin of the "Radio Club Of America" have shown that the traditional ground radial system composed of a number of buried or surface wires can be equalled or bettered by the use of an elevated ground screen situated about 6.5 feet (2m) above the earth's surface.(Fig. 10). The screen is composed of a number of radial wires, connected together at their extremities, running parallel to the ground. Ground screen efficiency is high as resistive losses are low, and the screen shields the antenna return currents from the poorly conducting ground beneath the screen. The earth currents which normally return

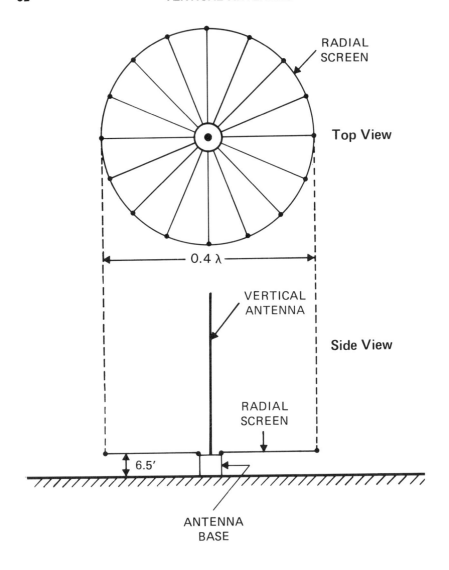

Fig. 10 Ideal ground screen consists of 50 insulated wires run radially out from vertical antenna base. Wires are connected together at their outer and inner tips. If possible, radial screen should be elevated, although good results have been obtained with screen lying on the ground, or buried just below the surface. Each wire is 0.2 wavelength long.

to the antenna through the ground now enter the ground screen instead of the lossy earth. A ground screen composed of 50 insulated wires about 0.2 wavelength long fanning out from the base of the antenna makes a radio ground as effective as 120 buried radial wires.

Even though the ground screen takes up considerable real estate and is cumbersome to install, it is sometimes used on the 80 and 160 meter bands by DX-minded amateurs having vertical antennas.

A Practical Ground Screen

Experiments have been conducted with a wire mesh screen laid on the ground instead of suspended overhead. Robert Sherwood, WB0JGP, ran experiments on a 36 foot (11 m) high aluminum tubing vertical on 1.8, 3.6 and 7.2 MHz. Various shapes and sizes of ground screen under the antenna were tested to find a combination that provided a low loss, ground return circuit.

One of the best systems tested consisted of two lengths of chicken wire laid out under the antenna in a form of a cross, with the antenna at the center of the cross. One length of chicken wire was 45 x 2 feet (13.7 x 0.6 m) and the other was only 30 x 2 feet (9 x 0.6 m) because of space restrictions.

When compared to a theoretical antenna over perfect ground this wire installation provided a feedpoint resistance of 48 ohms on 40 meters, 9 ohms on 80 meters and 2 ohms on 160 meters. Antenna efficiency was 67 percent on 7.2 MHz, 62 percent on 3.6 MHz and 25 percent on 1.8 MHz.

The efficiency figure on 160 meters is not spectacular, but in order to raise it an appreciable amount a more complex ground system and higher antenna are required. Top loading would be of benefit, as would increasing the size of the ground screen.

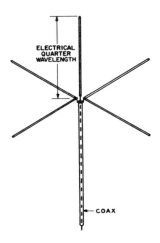

Fig. 11 Ground plane radials provide "radio ground" at the base of an elevated vertical antenna. Radials are resonant at the operating frequency. If a sufficient number of radials are used, no radiation takes place from them. A minimum of three radials is required and some amateurs prefer as many as six radials.

An additional aspect of wire screening is that it may be added to an existing ground radial system at little cost and effort. It also makes a good installation for a portable or Field Day site.

(This ground screen system is fully described in the May, 1977 issue of "Ham Radio" magazine.)

The Resonant Radial System

The resonant radial vertical antenna (popularly called the ground plane antenna) provides its own radio ground at the base of the antenna by virtue of quarter-wave, tuned radials run out in a horizontal plane beneath the antenna (Fig. 11). If a sufficient number of radials are used, no radiation takes place from them. A radio ground point is thus established at the base of the antenna where it is needed.

As the radials form a tuned system, they must be

isolated from ground and nearby metallic objects. The radial tips are "hot" with rf energy and should not be touched during transmitter operation.

In order to preserve the omni-directivity of the ground plane antenna, a minimum of three radials is required. Some amateurs prefer as many as six radials and most manufactured antennas have four radials. As long as there are three or more, the exact number of radials is unimportant when the antenna base is well clear of the ground.

Ground Loss Under the Ground Plane Antenna

Tests were run by Willy Sayer, WA6BAN, on a 7 MHz ground plane whose radials were 3.5 feet (1.1 m) above ground. An overall efficiency of 62 percent was measured when four radials were used, indicating about 38 percent of the output power was dissipated in ground loss. When the number of radials was increased to eleven, antenna efficiency increased to about 80 percent. Finally a total of 22 radials brought antenna efficiency up to over 90 percent. These results show that a large number of radials are required when a ground plane antenna is mounted close to the ground.

Sloping Radials

When the radials lie in the horizontal plane, no radiation takes place from them and the feedpoint resistance of the antennas is about 36 ohms. If the radials are sloped downwards (to act as supporting guy wires for the installation, for example), they begin to radiate as antenna sections and the radiation resistance of the ground plane antenna increases. When the radials slope downwards at an angle of about 40 degrees from the horizontal the feedpoint resistance of the ground plane antenna is a good match to the popular 50 ohm coaxial transmission line (see chapter 5).

The Radio Ground--The Final Word

Ground system losses dissipate a portion of the transmitter power, reducing the field radiated from the antenna. The losses are equivalent to the power dissipated in a resistor in series with the antenna radiation resistance. Local ground conductivity data is rarely available so the best possible ground system should be used with the vertical antenna.

George Brown of broadcast antenna fame summed it all up in 1937 when he said, "Too much emphasis cannot be given to the fact that, where direct field intensity along the ground is the sole aim, the ground system is of more importance than the antenna itself."

With regard to the higher frequency bands, where antenna size is relatively small, ground loss can be reduced by raising the vertical antenna and using a resonant radial system (ground plane) clear of the earth. This decreases the influence of the earth under the antenna and is the reason why three or four radials are sufficient for hf and vhf ground plane antennas mounted a half-wavelength or more above the earth.

Because the ground plane technique avoids most of the problems associated with a direct ground connection, it is a simple and practical device that can be used with success by radio amateurs on the hf and vhf bands. More about this popular antenna in a later chapter.

Summary: a ground screen is better than radials placed on, or just beneath, the surface of the ground. Radials are better than multiple ground rods. Longer radials are better than shorter ones. A lot of radials are better than a few. Multiple ground rods are better than a single ground rod. And a single ground rod is better than nothing! Resonant radials are discussed in chapter 5.

Chapter 3

Practical Marconi Antennas

Marconi found early in his experiments that if he grounded one terminal of his spark oscillator and connected the other to a vertical wire his radio range was greatly extended. He discovered that his antenna worked best when the length was a function of the wavelength of the transmitter. His tuning system was rudimentary and he probably did not comprehend what most amateurs understand today: any length of wire can be resonated to any frequency provided the correct tuning system is used.

The "Mirror Effect" of Ground

The fundamental antenna building block is the half-wave dipole, and most horizontal antennas are made up of half wave elements. However, the vertical antenna can take advantage of the ground which acts as an electrical mirror. If a quarter-wave vertical antenna is used, the mirror-effect makes up the missing quarter wave portion as shown in Chapter 1, Fig. 3. This is the basis of the Marconi antenna.

The current distribution in a quarter-wave Marconi antenna resembles that in half of a dipole, that is, a minimum value at the free end and a maximum at the base, or feed point. The rf voltage on the antenna, on the other hand, is a maximum value at the end and a minimum at the base.

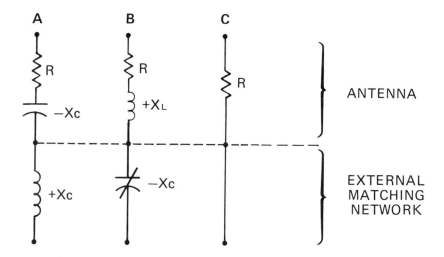

Fig. 1 Electrical characteristics of antenna can be visualized as resistor in series with reactance. The resistor represents the radiation resistance and the reactance represents the capacitive or inductive characteristic of the antenna. For a resonant antenna, the reactance is zero.

Radiation Resistance of an Antenna

The radiation resistance (R) at a point in an antenna can be described as the ratio of the voltage field about the antenna (E) divided by the current flowing in the antenna (I). Or, in terms of Ohm's Law, radiation resistance, R=E/I. At the high current feedpoint of the Marconi antenna, Ohm's law shows that the radiation resistance is low. As an example, a quarter-wave vertical Marconi antenna above perfect ground exhibits a radiation resistance half the value of a dipole, or about 36 ohms. Values of radiation resistance smaller than this figure are recorded for shorter antennas, and greater values are measured for antennas somewhat longer than a quarter wavelength. When the radiation resistance is measured at the feedpoint of the antenna it is called "feedpoint resistance".

The "Radio Ground"

Illustrations and discussions in this and following chapters refer to a "radio ground". This describes a ground termination for the antenna. It is usually located at the base of the vertical antenna and may consist of ground rods, radial wires, a ground screen, or a combination of all three. Refer to chapter 2 for a discussion of ground connections.

Antenna Reactance

Unless the antenna is resonant, a quality called "reactance" is found at the feedpoint. Reactance is the inertia offered to the flow of rf current through a coil or capacitor that plays a part similar to resistance in a dc circuit. Reactance is measured in ohms, just as in the case of resistance. The amount of reactance at the feedpoint of an antenna is a function of antenna length and diameter. When the antenna is shorter than resonance, the reactance is negative (capacitive) and when longer, reactance is positive (inductive). At antenna resonance, reactance is zero.

At frequencies near resonance, an antenna can be considered as a circuit consisting of a resistance and reactance in series (Fig. 1). To establish a match to the transmitter or to a coax line, the antenna reactance must be cancelled by an equal reactance of the opposite sign. This is accomplished by the addition of an external network to the antenna circuit. The network may be as simple as a loading coil or as complex as an impedance matching tuner.

The Quarter-wave Marconi Antenna for the Low Bands

A good Marconi antenna for the lower frequency amateur bands consists of a quarter-wavelength wire

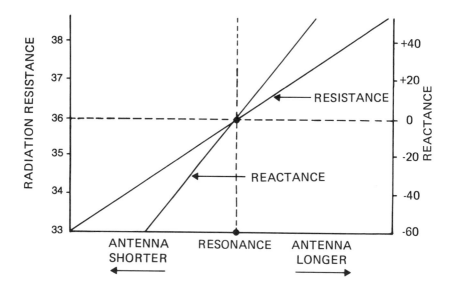

Fig. 2 Radiation resistance and reactance of antenna are a function of antenna length and diameter. The shorter the antenna, the lower the radiation resistance and the higher the loss due to ground resistance.

used with a ground termination. Its main virtue is that it is cheap and easy to erect and its main disadvantage is that it is subject to high ground losses unless carefully installed.

In practice, the wire may be any length from a small fraction of a wavelength to many wavelengths, and still be classified as a Marconi antenna. Radiation resistance and reactance of a Marconi antenna are a function of length as illustrated in Fig. 2, and it is easy to see that the shorter the antenna, the lower the radiation resistance and the higher the loss due to ground resistance.

A Marconi antenna for the lower frequency amateur bands is shown in Fig. 3. The far portion of the antenna may run parallel to the earth to reduce overall antenna height. Only the vertical portion of the antenna provides low-angle radiation. The

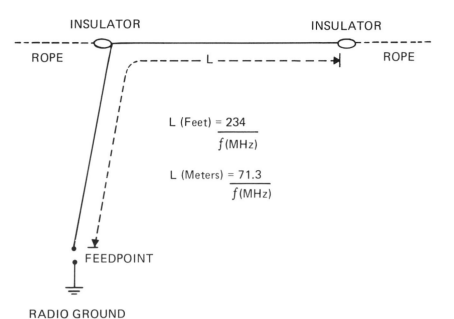

Fig. 3 A simple wire Marconi antenna for the low frequency amateur bands. Only the vertical portion of the antenna provides low-angle radiation. Horizontal portion provides some high angle, horizontally polarized radiation. Antenna should be suspended so that horizontal portion is 20 to 50 feet above ground.

horizontal section provides some horizontally polarized, high angle radiation but because the current in this portion of the antenna is low, radiation is also low.

As the horizontal portion of the antenna increases at the expense of the vertical section, the radiation resistance of the antenna decreases, as it is a function of the ratio of the vertical height to the operating wavelength.

A simple installation is a quarter wavelength wire suspended 20 to 50 feet (6 to 15 m) in the air. The radiation resistance is of the order of 10 to 15 ohms and average ground losses bring the feedpoint resistance close to 25 ohms. The antenna can be

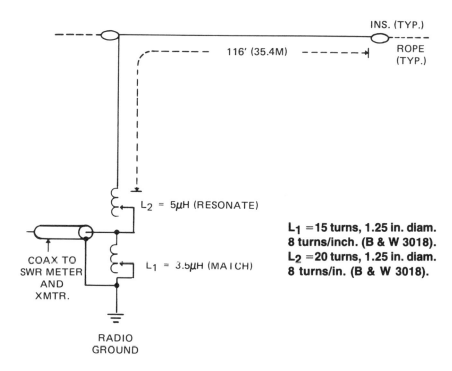

Fig. 4 A practical Marconi antenna with matching system for 160 meter operation. Antenna resonance is established with series inductor and match is adjusted with shunt-connected coil.

matched to a 50 ohm feed system by a simple network which consists of the antenna itself plus a shunt coil across the feedpoint. The antenna is cut slightly shorter than resonance to provide a degree of capacitive reactance, and the shunt inductor cancels this reactance. This action provides an equivalent circuit with a feed point resistance of 50 ohms.

A Practical 160 Meter Marconi Antenna

A 160 meter version of the basic Marconi antenna has a passband between the 2-to-1 SWR points as measured on the coax feedline of about 70 kHz. That is, when the antenna is adjusted for 1965 kHz, it will provide low SWR over the range of about 1930 to 2000 kHz (Fig.4). The natural resonant frequency of the antenna is higher than normal (about 2.02 MHz) and is lowered in frequency by the addition of a series-connected loading coil (RESONATE) at the feedpoint of the antenna. Antenna resonance can be established down to 1800 kHz with this coil and impedance matching is accomplished with shunt coil (MATCH).

Antenna adjustment is simple and rapid. The feedline is disconnected from the antenna and a two turn coil between antenna feedpoint and ground is temporarily installed instead of L1. A dip meter is coupled to the coil. The frequency of the dip meter is checked in a nearby receiver. The loading coil (RESONATE) is adjusted for resonance at 1965 kHz and the coil L1 is replaced in the circuit. The shunt coil (MATCH) is now adjusted for lowest SWR on the coaxial line to the transmitter. The coil settings are logged and the transmitter moved lower in frequency by 25 kHz. Resonance is again established by adding turns to coil L2 and the new coil setting logged. (The setting of coil L1 may have to be adjusted slightly.) This process is repeated at 25 kHz intervals down to 1800 kHz. Finally, a tuning chart is made to permit quick frequency changes. Once a particular resonant frequency logging has been established for the antenna, frequency excursions of up to plus or minus 25 kHz may be made from this point with no adjustment to the inductors.

As pointed out in the previous chapter, it is a good idea to decouple the transmitter from the equipment ground by winding the power cord of the unit around a ferrite core. This makes the radio ground do its job and reduces the chances of RFI and TVI caused by unwanted coupling between the transmitter and the power line.

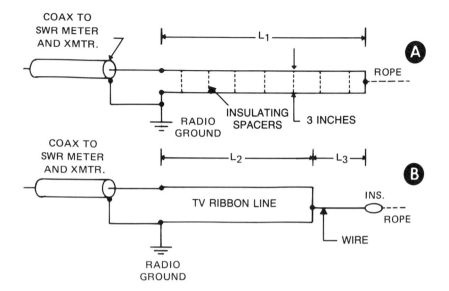

FREQ. (MHz)	L1	L2	L3
1.85	126.5	109.0	18.0
1.95	120.0	104.0	16.0
3.60	65.0	53.3	11.7
3.80	61.5	50.4	11.1
7.10	32.9	27.0	5.9
10.1	23.2	19.0	4.2
14.1	16.6	13.6	3.0
18.1	12.9	10.6	2.3
21.2	11.0	9.0	2.0
24.9	9.4	7.7	1.7
28.6	8.2	6.7	1.5
50.1	4.7	3.9	0.8

(FEET X 0.348 = METERS)

Fig. 5 The folded Marconi antenna provides feedpoint resistance step-up by a factor of four. This antenna having a feedpoint resistance of 15 ohms will have a value of 60 ohms when a two wire arrangement is used. Second wire is grounded at the feedpoint. Antenna may be made of TV "ribbon line" if velocity of line is taken into consideration as shown in drawing (B).

The Folded Marconi Antenna

A good way to make the Marconi antenna less vulnerable to ground resistance is to raise its feedpoint resistance. This can be done by making the antenna out of two equal-length, closely spaced quarter-wavelength wires connected in parallel at the far end (Fig. 5A). Antenna current is divided between the wires when one is fed and the other grounded at the feedpoint. The feedpoint resistance of the combination is increased by a factor of four over a single wire. Thus a 15 ohm Marconi antenna will have a feedpoint resistance of 15x4=60 ohms when the two-wire antenna is substituted for it. This is a good design to use if the height above ground of the horizontal portion of the antenna is small.

The "Ribbon" Folded Marconi Antenna

The folded Marconi antenna can be made of a length of TV "ribbon line" if the velocity factor of the line is taken into consideration. For 300 ohm flat line, the factor is 0.82 and this portion of the antenna (L2) is made of tv ribbon line, with the remaining section (L3) consisting of a single wire (Fig. 5B). Representative antenna dimensions for the lower frequency amateur bands are shown in the illustration.

The Extended Marconi Antenna

Another technique used to boost the radiation resistance of the Marconi antenna is to extend the length beyond a quarter-wavelength. Two lengths that work well are 0.28 and 0.31 wavelength. The first length provides a close match to a 50 ohm coax line and the second to a 75 ohm line. Both designs require a series tuning capacitor to cancel the inductive reactance, and to establish antenna

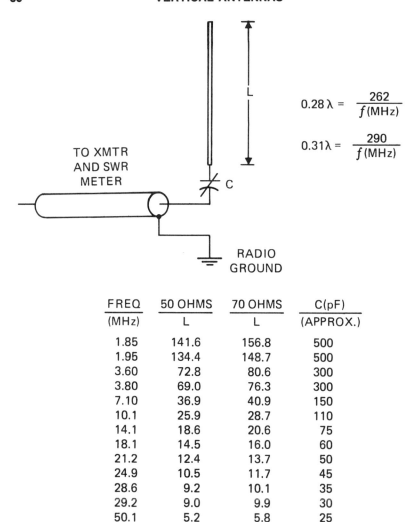

$$0.28\,\lambda = \frac{262}{f\,(\text{MHz})}$$

$$0.31\lambda = \frac{290}{f\,(\text{MHz})}$$

TO XMTR
AND SWR
METER

RADIO
GROUND

FREQ	50 OHMS	70 OHMS	C(pF)
(MHz)	L	L	(APPROX.)
1.85	141.6	156.8	500
1.95	134.4	148.7	500
3.60	72.8	80.6	300
3.80	69.0	76.3	300
7.10	36.9	40.9	150
10.1	25.9	28.7	110
14.1	18.6	20.6	75
18.1	14.5	16.0	60
21.2	12.4	13.7	50
24.9	10.5	11.7	45
28.6	9.2	10.1	35
29.2	9.0	9.9	30
50.1	5.2	5.8	25

(FEET X 0.3048 = METERS)

Fig. 6 Extended Marconi antenna is longer than a quarter-wavelength. Length is chosen so as to match either a 50 or 75 ohm coax line. Series capacitor tunes out inductive reactance of antenna.

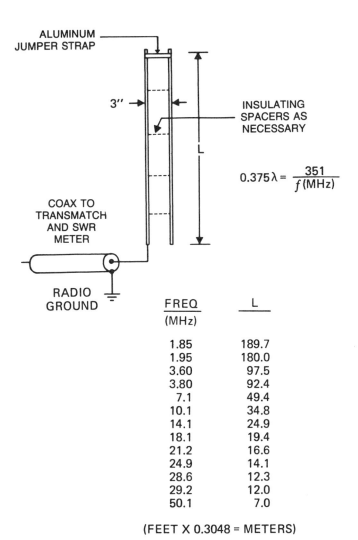

ALUMINUM
JUMPER STRAP

3"

INSULATING
SPACERS AS
NECESSARY

L

$$0.375\lambda = \frac{351}{f\,(MHz)}$$

COAX TO
TRANSMATCH
AND SWR
METER

RADIO
GROUND

FREQ (MHz)	L
1.85	189.7
1.95	180.0
3.60	97.5
3.80	92.4
7.1	49.4
10.1	34.8
14.1	24.9
18.1	19.4
21.2	16.6
24.9	14.1
28.6	12.3
29.2	12.0
50.1	7.0

(FEET X 0.3048 = METERS)

Fig. 7 The extended, folded Marconi antenna provides high step-up of feed-point resistance. Unfed wire is not grounded. If all of the antenna is vertical, the feedpoint resistance is about 145 ohms.

resonance. The capacitor setting and antenna length are adjusted for lowest value of SWR on the line from antenna to transmitter. Fig. 6 provides typical antenna dimensions for the hf bands.

Both of these extended antennas are very effective and their use is recommended provided a good ground is used and enough real estate is available for installation.

The Extended, Folded Marconi Antenna

A folded version of the extended Marconi antenna is shown in Fig. 7. The antenna is 0.375 wavelength long. Notice that the unfed wire is not grounded, as is the case with the shorter, folded antenna design. Because the currents in the two wires are not equal at a given distance from the feedpoint, use of tv ribbon line is not recommended. A practical design consists of two no. 12 wires or aluminum tubing, separated by 3 inch (7.6 cm) insulating spacers. Feedpoint resistance of this antenna is about 145 ohms if the whole antenna is vertical, dropping to about 60 to 80 ohms, depending upon the ratio of vertical to horizontal length. Because of the high feedpoint resistance, this antenna is recommended for use in areas with high values of ground resistance. A matching transformer can be used at the base of the antenna, or a Transmatch at the station end of the line will reduce the system SWR to a small value.

The Very Short Marconi Antenna

In some cases is is impossible to put up a full-size Marconi antenna and a shorter version is required. There is nothing wrong with this, provided the user understands the tradeoffs involved. As the Marconi is shortened below quarter-wave resonance, the radiation resistance drops rapidly and capacitive (negative) reactance increases (see Fig. 2). Reducing the antenna size to one-eighth wavelength, for example, drops the feedpoint resistance from 36 ohms to a value of about 8 ohms. The capacitive reactance increases from zero to about -400 ohms, the exact value depending upon conductor diameter. When the reactance is cancelled out, the same value of ground resistance provides a loss about two and a half times greater than that realized with a full size antenna. It takes a very good ground system and an efficient matching network to make a short Marconi antenna work as well as a long one. Nevertheless, a short antenna can be very useful if nothing else is available.

Making the Short Antenna Work

To resonate a short Marconi antenna, the missing portion of the antenna takes the form of a loading coil, or inductance, placed in series with the antenna. Ideally, the coil should be air wound, or wound on a ceramic form, and be inclosed in an insulating, waterproof container.

A desirable goal of loading is to increase the effective length of the antenna carrying the greatest portion of the current. A loading coil can be placed at any point in the antenna but is most effective when it is placed at, or near, the center point.

When the coil is placed near the feedpoint of the antenna, current through the coil is high and coil losses are correspondingly high. The greater the distance of the coil from the feedpoint, the lower the current in the coil and the lower the coil losses, but the larger the coil must be to maintain resonance. Theoretically, if the coil were located at the end of the antenna, it would be infinite in size. As a result, a compromise between coil size and loss indicates placement near the center point

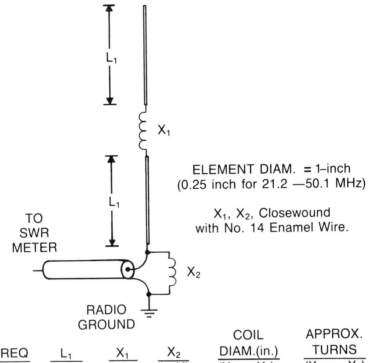

ELEMENT DIAM. = 1–inch
(0.25 inch for 21.2 —50.1 MHz)

X_1, X_2, Closewound
with No. 14 Enamel Wire.

FREQ	L_1	X_1	X_2	COIL DIAM.(in.)		APPROX. TURNS	
(MHz)	(FT.)	(μH)	(μH)	(X_1	X_2)	(X_1	X_2)
1.85	31.62	71.4	3.8	3	2	30	7
1.95	30.00	67.2	3.6	2	2	28	7
3.6	16.25	32.9	1.9	2	2	30	5
3.8	15.40	30.9	1.8	2	2	29	5
7.1	8.23	14.8	1.0	2	2	17	3
10.1	5.79	9.7	0.7	2	1	13	4
14.1	4.14	6.5	0.5	2	1	10	4
18.1	3.23	4.8	0.4	2	1	8	3
21.2	2.75	3.9	0.3	2	1	7	3
24.9	2.34	3.3	0.3	2	1	7	2
28.6	2.00	2.9	0.3	1	1	11	2
29.6	1.97	2.7	0.2	1	1	10	2
50.1	1.16	1.4	0.1	1	1	6	2

(FEET X 0.3048 = METERS)

Fig. 8 Center loaded element makes short antenna practical. Data is given for all high frequency bands. Design frequency for each band is indicated. Adjusting top section of antenna or number of turns in loading coil will move design frequency higher or lower in the band. Base shunt coil provides impedance match to 50 or 75 ohm coax line.

* * * *

of the antenna. For mechanical reasons, however, the coil is often placed at the base of the antenna with good results.

Shown in Figs. 8 and 9 are coil-loaded antenna designs for the high frequency bands that allow the user to build a Marconi antenna of moderate size. Element diameter is 1-inch (2.54 cm). A larger diameter element requires slightly less inductance in the loading coil, whereas a smaller diameter element requires more inductance. Feedpoint resistance of these antennas is quite low and they are matched to a 50 or 75 ohm coax line with a simple L-network matching coil, as described elsewhere in this handbook.

Building a Coil-loaded Antenna

A popular and practical mechanical design for a coil-loaded vertical antenna is shown in Fig. 10. The lower section of the assembly is made of sections of a heavy-duty, TV-type "slip-up" mast and the top section above the coil is made up of lengths of telescoping aluminum tubing. The antenna is held in position by three guy wires attached just below the loading coil.

Coil construction depends upon size. The assembly must be rugged as it supports the antenna section above it. A practical design makes use of a section of PVC plastic pipe which forms a connection between the two antenna halves. It may have to be shimmed to

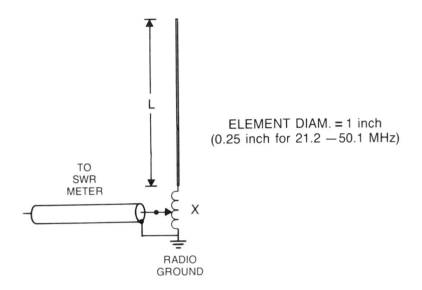

ELEMENT DIAM. = 1 inch
(0.25 inch for 21.2 — 50.1 MHz)

FREQ (MHz)	L (FT)	X (μ H)	COIL DATA
1.85	30	87	100 Turns, 2'' Diam., 10 Turns/inch
1.85	50	52	B & W 3907-1 or Equiv.
1.95	30	78	(89 μ H)
1.95	50	46	80 Turns, 2'' Diam., 8 Turns/inch
3.5	30	21	B & W 3900 or Equiv. (57 μ H)
3.5	50	8.0	
4.0	30	1.5	
4.0	50	3.8	
7.1	20	5.8	
14.0	10	2.6	40 Turns, 1 1/8'' Diam., 4 Turns/inch
18.1	10	1.0	B & W 1204T or Equiv. (8.3 μ H)
21.2	8	1.3	
24.9	8	0.5	
28.6	5	1.4	
29.6	5	1.2	
50.1	2	1.2	

(FEET X 0.3048 = METERS)

Fig. 9 Base loaded element provides simple antenna with only one matching and loading inductance. Number of turns or antenna length is adjusted for resonance. Tap point on base coil is adjusted for impedance match to 50 or 75 ohm coax line.

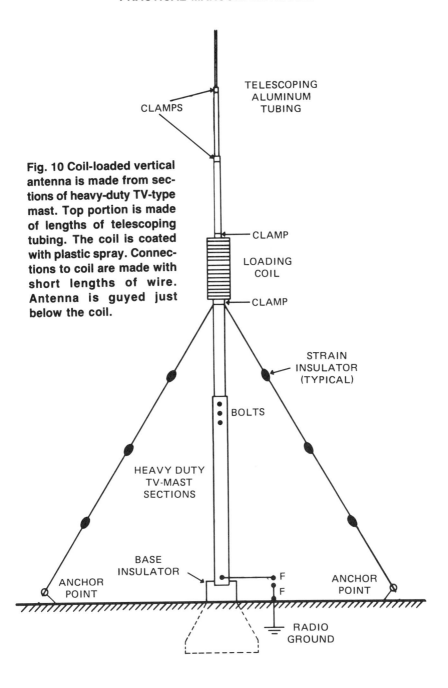

Fig. 10 Coil-loaded vertical antenna is made from sections of heavy-duty TV-type mast. Top portion is made of lengths of telescoping tubing. The coil is coated with plastic spray. Connections to coil are made with short lengths of wire. Antenna is guyed just below the coil.

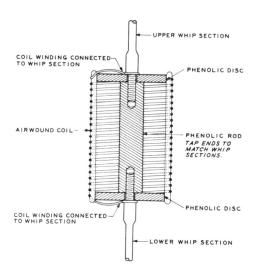

Fig. 11 Loading coil for small antenna can be made of air wound stock supported by insulating discs cemented to a center support rod. Heavy copper wire or strap makes connections between coil and antenna sections.

make a glove-fit to the smaller-diameter top section.

An alternative design is to use an air-wound coil supported by home-made insulating discs that are cemented to a center phenolic rod. The rod is drilled to fit the antenna sections, as shown in Fig. 11. This is a good arrangement for mobile antennas, but can be modified for larger fixed station antennas as well.

When the loading coil is completed, it must be given a protective coat of clear polyurethane or other liquid plastic. Connections between the coil and the antenna sections are made by short lengths of heavy copper wire or strap.

The antenna is now adjusted to the operating frequency by placing a two turn loop of wire between the feedpoint and ground. A dip meter is coupled to

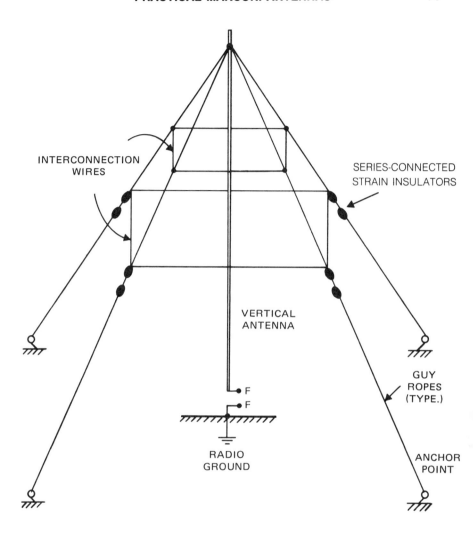

INTERCONNECTION
WIRES

SERIES-CONNECTED
STRAIN INSULATORS

VERTICAL
ANTENNA

GUY
ROPES
(TYPE.)

F
F

RADIO
GROUND

ANCHOR
POINT

Fig. 12 Sloping loading wires add electrical length to short vertical antenna and also provide capacitive loading. Wires are interconnected at midpoints and the ends.

the coil and the top section of the antenna is varied in length, or the number of turns on the coil adjusted, to achieve resonance.

The Top-loaded Vertical Antenna

An interesting form of top-loading that does not require a coil is shown in Fig. 12. Sloping loading wires add electrical length to the vertical antenna while also providing capacitive loading, both of which lower the natural self-resonant frequency of the antenna. The wires are interconnected at the midpoints and the ends. Multiple loading wires can be used to advantage to serve as guy wires for the vertical section. Optimum length of the loading wires will vary from one installation to another and wire length will have to be determined by user experimentation.

A Compact Top Hat Antenna for 160 Meters

Shown in Fig. 13 is a compact, 28 foot (8.53m) high, top-loaded vertical antenna. With changes in the matching network, it will also work on 80 meters as well as 160.

The antenna consists of three sections of aluminum tubing, ranging from 2.5 inches (63.5 mm) diameter at the base to 1.625 inches (41.3 mm) diameter for the top section. A short top mast section made of 1-inch (25.4 mm) diameter tubing provides support for the top hat guys. Sections are shimmed and bolted to establish a firm fit.

The top hat is 17 feet (5.21 m) in diameter and consists of a 12-inch (30 cm) diameter aluminum center plate with six outriggers, guyed to the top of the mast. The hat is made of lengths of 1/4-inch (6.4 mm) diameter tubing formed into three arcs, connected to the mast with 1/2-inch (12.7 mm) tubing. The hat requires six outriggers spaced 60 degrees apart.

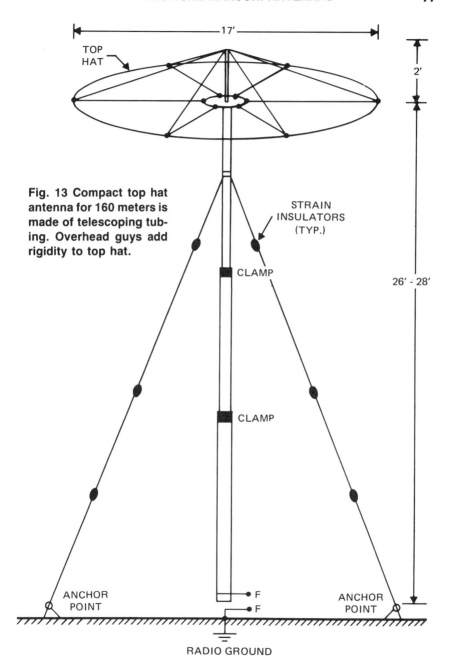

TOP HAT

Fig. 13 Compact top hat antenna for 160 meters is made of telescoping tubing. Overhead guys add rigidity to top hat.

STRAIN INSULATORS (TYP.)

CLAMP

CLAMP

ANCHOR POINT

ANCHOR POINT

RADIO GROUND

Top Hat Assembly

The top hat is made up as a separate assembly. The radial arms are bolted to an aluminum center disc which is drilled to pass the antenna. It is attached to the antenna by an aluminum fitting 2" (5 cm) high with a wall thickness of 0.5" (1.3 cm). It is machined to glove-fit over the antenna.

The top mast is attached to the top of the vertical section and aluminum fence wire is run from it to the end of each outrigger to add rigidity to the top hat. The antenna is guyed near the top by three guy wires, broken up with strain insulators placed at 8 foot (2.4 m) intervals.

Input resistance at resonance of the antenna is about 5 ohms. It is matched to the feedline by means of an L-network of the type discussed in chapter 4. (This antenna is based on an original design by Jerry Sevick, W2FMI, shown in the January, 1976, issue of "QST" magazine).

The Helically Loaded Vertical Antenna

Resonance can be established at a given frequency by the use of a short, helically-wound element (Fig. 14). Treated bamboo poles, PVC plastic tubing, or fiberglass quad antenna spreaders, can be used as a form on which to wind the helix. Diameter of the helix must be small in relation to length and a practical design makes use of a one inch (25.4 mm) winding form. A helix length of about .05 wavelength or more provides good results as a substitute for a full-size quarter wavelength vertical antenna.

The amount of wire required for the winding depends upon helix length and pitch (turns per inch). In general, a half-wavelength of no. 14 Formvar-coated wire is spirally wrapped on the form, with turn spacing approximately equal to the wire diameter. This amount of wire will approximate a quarter-wave resonance.

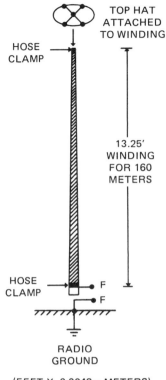

TOP HAT
ATTACHED
TO WINDING

HOSE
CLAMP

13.25'
WINDING
FOR 160
METERS

HOSE
CLAMP

F

F

RADIO
GROUND

(FEET X 0.3048 = METERS)

Fig. 14 Helix antenna for 160 meters is wound on tapered form. Small top hat is used to prevent high voltage corona discharge from top of the antenna.

In order to prevent any high voltage corona discharge, a 12-inch (30 cm) diameter wire top hat is attached to the helix. Antenna resonance can be adjusted by varying the size of the hat, or by adding a small extra inductance at the base of the antenna.

Before weatherproofing, the helical antenna is mounted in place, with the ground system installed. A dip meter is connected to a two-turn loop placed between the feedpoint and ground. Antenna resonance is determined and a few turns are added or removed

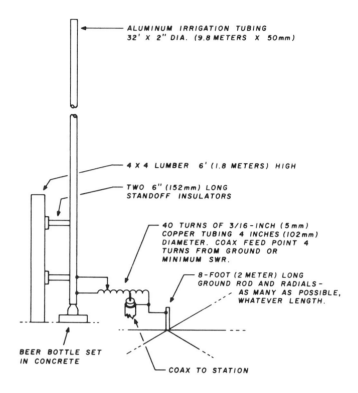

ALUMINUM IRRIGATION TUBING
32' X 2" DIA. (9.8 METERS X 50mm)

4 X 4 LUMBER 6' (1.8 METERS) HIGH

TWO 6" (152mm) LONG
STANDOFF INSULATORS

40 TURNS OF 3/16-INCH (5mm)
COPPER TUBING 4 INCHES (102mm)
DIAMETER. COAX FEED POINT 4
TURNS FROM GROUND OR
MINIMUM SWR.

8-FOOT (2 METER) LONG
GROUND ROD AND RADIALS-
AS MANY AS POSSIBLE,
WHATEVER LENGTH.

BEER BOTTLE SET
IN CONCRETE

COAX TO STATION

Fig. 15 Inexpensive base-loaded 160 meter vertical antenna uses section of aluminum irrigation tubing. Taps on loading coil allow adjustments for resonance and impedance matching.

from the top of the helix until the antenna is resonant at the desired operating frequency.

Feedpoint resistance of a helical antenna is quite low, of the order of 5 to 10 ohms, depending upon helix length. An L-network, of the type described in chapter 4, can be used to match the antenna to a 50 ohm transmission line.

When the antenna is completed, it should be given several coats of spar varnish to weatherproof the antenna and to hold the helix turns in position.

A Base-loaded Vertical for 160 Meters

While a center-loaded vertical antenna provides higher efficiency than a base loaded one, a simple base-loaded antenna is unobtrusive and inexpensive to build and erect. The antenna is designed by Ed Marriner, W6XM, and described in the August, 1980 issue of "Ham Radio" magazine.

The antenna consists of a 32 foot (9.8 m) section of 2-inch (50.8 mm) diameter aluminum irrigation tubing supported on a post sunk into the ground. The assembly of the antenna is shown in Fig. 15.

Antenna resonance is established by a loading coil placed at the base of the antenna. For highest efficiency, it is wound with 3/16-inch (5.0 mm) diameter copper tubing. A 4-inch (101.6 mm) diameter section of water pipe is used as a mandrel. The coil has 40 turns.

A support is made for the coil from three pieces of plastic 1-inch (25.4 mm) wide. The supports are long enough so that holes drilled in them separate the coil turns by about the diameter of the tubing. After the coil is wound, the pieces are threaded onto the coil and fastened in place with epoxy cement.

Antenna adjustment is accomplished by shorting the antenna and loading coil to ground via a two turn coil. The loading coil turns are adjusted for resonance with a dip meter. Wide copper straps are soldered to the coil once the proper taps are found. The transmission line is tapped near the ground end of the coil and the point adjusted for lowest SWR on the transmission line. The tap point will depend upon the resistance of the ground system, but will be about four turns from the bottom of the coil.

The antenna uses five radials about 30 feet (9.1 m) long, laid upon the ground, plus an 8-foot (2.4 m) ground rod at the base of the antenna.

A Large Vertical for 160 and 80 Meters

This DX antenna for the low bands is described   by Harry Hyder, W7IV, in   the May,   1975, issue   of "Ham Radio"   magazine (Fig. 16). Overall height is 91 feet (27.7 m) and consists of a 70 foot (21.3 m)   aluminum lattice tower   surmounted   by a 21 foot (6.4 m) whip. It   is   0.347   wavelength   on   80   meters   and   0.166 wavelength   on   160 meters.   Sixteen radials 125 feet (38.1 m) long are buried in   shallow trenches   about the   antenna.   The input resistance   of   the   antenna (including ground resistance)   is   about   14 ohms   on 160 meters and 187 ohms on 80 meters.

The   aluminum tower is   11 inches (27.9 cm)   on   a side   and weighs about 100 pounds. It is guyed at two levels   with   three guy wires,   broken   up   with   egg insulators.

An inductor of   about   14   microhenries tunes   the tower   to 1.8 mHz and the   feedline   is tapped on the lower end   of the coil to provide a good match to the coaxial feedline.

A   300 pF   variable series capacitor resonates the antenna to   the   80   meter band   and band   change   is accomplished by a remote-control relay.

The SWR   is   below   1.3-to-1   across the   80 meter band and below 1.5-to-1 from 1.8 to 1.9 MHz.

A Top-loaded Marconi for 80 Meters

This unusual   top-loaded   antenna   is hung   from a branch   of   a   tall tree.   It   is   designed   by   Henry Elwell,   W2MB,   and   is   described in   the September, 1971 issue of "Ham Radio" magazine.

Installation of   the   antenna is shown in   Fig. 17. A   rope and pulley   placed at the   65   foot   (19.8 m) elevation   in   the   tree   simplifies   the   antenna installation.

The top   disc   is made   of   two   6   foot   (1.8   m) lengths of   light   wood   strapped   in   the form of   a

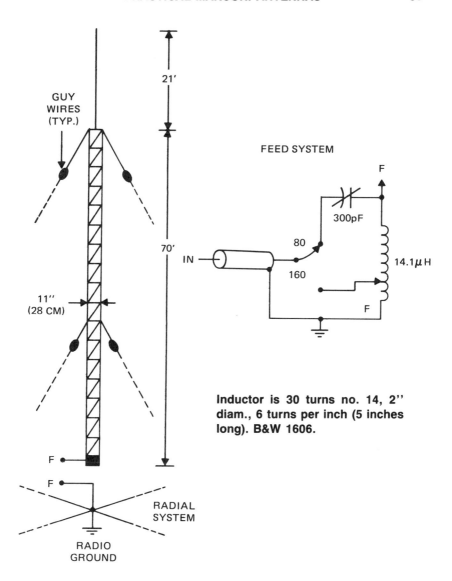

Inductor is 30 turns no. 14, 2''
diam., 6 turns per inch (5 inches
long). B&W 1606.

**Fig. 16 DX vertical antenna operates on both 80 and 160 meter bands. A
21 foot whip is mounted to top of light duty, 70 foot guyed aluminum tower.
Adjustable base network provides two-band operation. Tower is guyed at
two levels for best stability in heavy winds.**

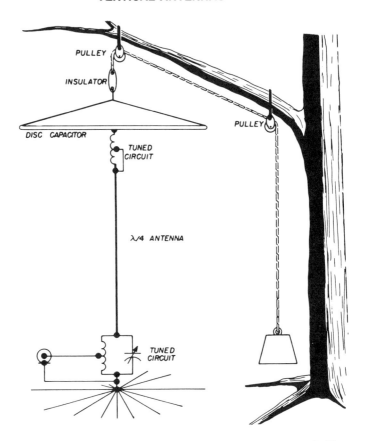

Fig. 17 Tree-supported 80 meter vertical antenna is loaded to half wave resonance by large top hat and loading coil. High impedance at base is matched to coax line by a parallel tuned circuit. Smaller top hat can be used with larger loading inductance, if desired.

cross. A 28 foot (8.5 m) length of 1/4-inch (6.3 mm) copper tubing is affixed to the cross by tie wires and twenty-four lengths of no. 12 copper wire are connected from the outside to the center of the disc. The loading coil has an inductance of about 44 microhenries.

When properly adjusted, the antenna provides half-wave resonance at the operating frequency and the feedpoint resistance is quite high. A parallel

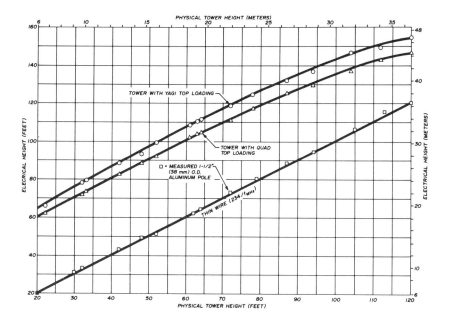

Fig. 18 Relationship between physical and electrical height of tower when loaded by either 3-element Yagi or 2-element Quad. Comparison curve for vertical wire is also shown.

tuned circuit at the base provides system resonance. The feedline is tapped on the coil at a point which provides a low value of SWR on the feedline at antenna resonance.

The ground system consists of 24 radials, each 66 feet (20 m) long made of aluminum wire fanning out from the antenna on the surface of the ground.

Use Your Beam Tower for the Low Bands

Why not use your existing beam tower as a vertical antenna for the low bands? It is possible and practical to use a beam tower as a vertical antenna, even though the tower may be grounded at the base. Best of all, the electrical height of the tower is increased by virtue of the top loading effect of the beam antenna. Data on feeding towers is given in chapter 4.

The chart of Fig. 18 shows a typical relationship of electrical height to tower height of a tower one to two feet (30 to 61 cm) on a side, top loaded with either a 3-element Yagi or a 2-element Quad beam. A comparison curve for a thin wire antenna is also shown. Multi-element Quads seem to add little top loading, possibly because the outer elements are removed from the tower and insulated from it. A large Yagi beam, on the other hand, provides additional loading over that shown in the graph.

As an example, a 70 foot (21.3 cm) tower top loaded with a Yagi antenna has an electrical height of about 118 feet (40 m).

A grounded base, shunt fed tower is a popular installation as it provides protection against lightning by channeling static electricity in the atmosphere directly to ground. (This material is abstracted from an article on shunt-fed antenna towers by John True, W4OQ, in the May, 1975, issue of "Ham Radio" magazine.)

Decoupling the Marconi Antenna From the House Wiring

The Marconi antenna is a good one for the 160 and 80 meter bands if the operator is pressed for space. An efficient radio ground is required and care must be taken to decouple the antenna system from the equipment ground and the power line. If the Marconi is close to the residence, and if open house wiring is used in the structure, it is possible to get inductive coupling between the antenna and the wiring. Some operators running high power in a 160 meter antenna have found to their dismay that various lights in the house go on when they are on the air!

The house wiring can be easily detuned to prevent this undesirable coupling by placing bypass capacitors across a few 120 volt outlets in the house. An easy way to accomplish this is to mount a .01 uF, 1.6 kV disc ceramic capacitor in an empty line plug and move it from one wall receptacle to another until the lights remain out when the transmitter is on.

Even though the 160 meter band is far removed from the television channels, it is still a good idea to use a low-pass TV filter on the transmitter to supress unwanted harmonics that might interfere with TV or FM reception.

A Top-hat Antenna for 75-80 Meters

This inexpensive top-hat antenna is designed for DX work on the 3.5 to 4.0 MHz band. Operating bandwidth is about 85 kHz between the 2-to-1 SWR points on the transmission line. If an auxiliary matching unit is used at the station, the antenna can operate over the whole 80 meter band. The design frequency is 3.85 MHz and operation at the low end of the band (without a matching unit) requires the addition of a small loading coil at the base of the antenna.

The antenna consists of a 35 foot (10.7 m) long, 2-inch (50.8 mm) diameter section of aluminum irrigation pipe top loaded by a hat made of four 8 foot (2.44 m) pieces of 3/4-inch (19.1 mm) diameter aluminum tubing, mounted at right angles to themselves and to the pipe (Fig. 19).

The irrigation pipe is very flexible and must be guyed at the top and two intermediate levels to prevent vibration in the wind. The antenna is mounted on a small block of wood to insulate it from ground. The wood is given several coats of clear epoxy or spar varnish to protect it from the weather.

The feedpoint resistance of the antenna is about

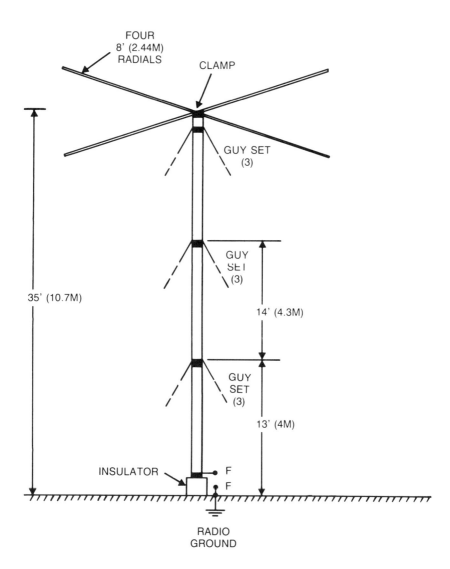

Fig. 19 Simple top hat antenna for 75-80 meters is only 35 feet high. Single section of aluminum irrigation pipe is used as radiator. Antenna is guyed at three points to prevent vibration in heavy wind.

20 ohms so an L-network, such as described in chapter 4, can be used to match the antenna to a coax line.

The Ground System

A ground screen is placed beneath the antenna. It consists of a number of 90 foot (27.4 m) radials fanning out from the antenna base. Either aluminum, copper or galvanized iron wire can be used, laid on the surface of the ground. The original antenna, designed and used by W7DHD, employed 100 radials varying in length from 90 feet (27.4 m) down to 65 feet (19.8 m).

The inner ends of the radials are attached to an 18 inch (0.5 m) square sheet of 1/4-inch (6.35 mm) thick aluminum drilled around the four edges for stainless steel bolts. After the wires are attached to the plate, it is given a heavy coat of asphalt roof sealer to protect it from ground moisture. The shield of the coax feedline is attached to the plate.

The outer ends of the radials are terminated by 18 inch (0.5 m) ground rods, cut from reinforcing steel. The shorter radials are provided with 4 foot (2.4 m) long rods. The center plate is grounded with one or two 8 foot (2.44 m) long rods for lightning protection. (This antenna is described in the June, 1983 issue of "Ham Radio" magazine.)

Using the Antenna on 160 Meters

Once the antenna is operating properly on 80 meters, an add-on modification will permit 160 meter operation. For the "top band", an 80 meter trap and auxiliary top-hat are added to the top of the antenna. Switching between bands is automatic, and the addition does not affect 80 meter operation.

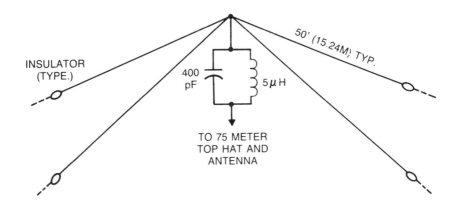

Fig. 20 Add-on modification allows antenna of Fig. 19 to be used on 160 meter band. Auxiliary top hat is electrically switched in and out when frequency of operation is changed.

The add-on modification is shown in Fig. 20. Four 50 foot (15.24 m) long sections of no. 8 or 10 aluminum clothesline wire serve as top guys and as the 160 meter top-hat. The trap is placed between the junction of these wires and the top of the antenna. The trap coil is about 5 microhenries and the parallel-connected capacitor is 400 pF, 5 kV. The trap is self-resonant at the 80 meter antenna design frequency. Before placing the trap atop the antenna, it is adjusted with the aid of a dip meter and nearby receiver.

The feedpoint resistance of the antenna on 160 meters is about 5 ohms and the use of a matching network is necessary.

A Hanging Top-Hat Antenna for 160 Meters

This interesting antenna was designed to be hung from the top branches of a tall tree or from a 70 foot (21.3 m) tower. It consists of a top-hat loading disc beneath which is a helical-wound loading coil about 20 feet (6 m) long. Overall

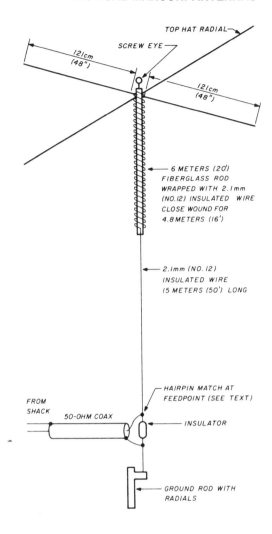

Fig. 21 Tree- or tower-mounted vertical antenna for 160 meters. Top hat and helix structure are supported by screw eye at top and connected to feedpoint with vertical wire.

antenna height is 70 feet. The antenna is base-fed
with a coax line and a shunt matching hairpin
inductor (Fig. 21).

In order to keep the maximum area of current
high in the air, the antenna is loaded to nearly
half-wave resonance by the inductor and top hat.
Operational bandwidth between the 2-to-1 SWR points
on the feedline is about 30 kHz with the antenna cut
for operation at the low frequency end of the band.

Antenna Construction

The form for the helical coil is a 20 foot (6 m)
length of fiberglass rod, 1.5 inches (3.8 cm) in
diameter. It is wound with about 260 feet (80 m) of
no. 12 insulated wire. The helix is closewound for
16 feet (4.8 m) and spacewound the diameter of the
wire for the rest of the winding. The spacewound
portion is at the top of the helix.

The top hat is built up of four foot (1.2 m)
lengths of aluminum tubing, 0.5-inch (1.2 cm) in
diameter. The tubes are attached to a metal ring
which is bolted to the top of the fiberglass pole.
The whole device is hung from a 10 foot (3 m)
sidearm mounted at the top of the tower.

Alternatively, it may be hung from the limb of a
tree by a rope and pulley combination. An eye bolt
affixed to the top of the pole allows the entire
antenna to be raised and lowered at will (Fig. 22).

When the helix coil is completed, it is covered
with three coats of polyurathane finish or spar
varnish. All bolts and electrical connections are
protected with a clear, silicone sealant, such as
General Electric RTV-108, or equivalent.

Tuning the Antenna

The antenna is tuned to 1815 kHz by shorting the
bottom end to the ground system via a two turn loop
coupled to a dip meter. Exact resonance is achieved

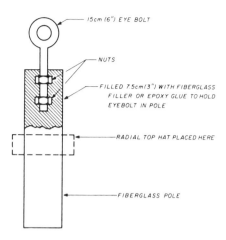

Fig. 22 Mechanical assembly of screw eye support for the antenna shown in Fig. 21.

by trimming the wire or by removing or adding a turn or two to the coil. Once resonance is established, match to the coax line is made by a shunt coil, or hairpin, placed across the feedpoint. It is designed to be employed with a multiple radial ground system. (This antenna was designed by Tony DePrato, WA4JQS, and was described in the March, 1980 issue of "Ham Radio Horizons" magazine.)

A Simple 80 and 160 Meter Vertical Antenna

This inexpensive and compact antenna is about 24 feet (7.3 m) high and is designed about a 20 foot (6.2 m) long piece of 2 inch (4.9 cm) diameter aluminum irrigation pipe, readily available from sprinkling equipment companies or farm equipment catalogs. A top loading coil resonates the antenna to 80 meters and a base coil adds sufficient loading for 160 meter operation.

Antenna assembly is shown in Fig. 23. The top loading coil is wound on a 20 inch (50.1 cm) length

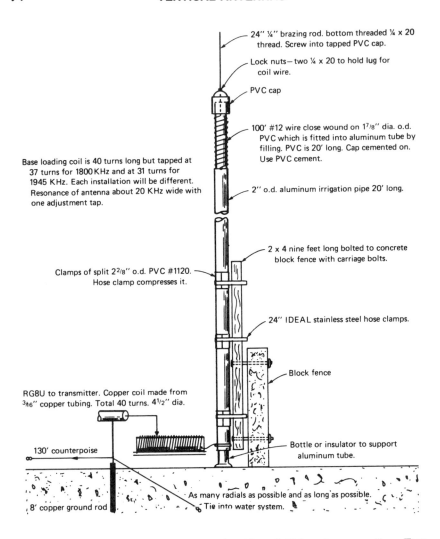

24" ¼" brazing rod. bottom threaded ¼ x 20 thread. Screw into tapped PVC cap.

Lock nuts—two ¼ x 20 to hold lug for coil wire.

PVC cap

100' #12 wire close wound on 1⁷/₈" dia. o.d. PVC which is fitted into aluminum tube by filling. PVC is 20' long. Cap cemented on. Use PVC cement.

Base loading coil is 40 turns long but tapped at 37 turns for 1800 KHz and at 31 turns for 1945 KHz. Each installation will be different. Resonance of antenna about 20 KHz wide with one adjustment tap.

2" o.d. aluminum irrigation pipe 20' long.

2 x 4 nine feet long bolted to concrete block fence with carriage bolts.

Clamps of split 2²/₈" o.d. PVC #1120. Hose clamp compresses it.

24" IDEAL stainless steel hose clamps.

Block fence

RG8U to transmitter. Copper coil made from ³/₁₆" copper tubing. Total 40 turns. 4¹/₂" dia.

130' counterpoise

Bottle or insulator to support aluminum tube.

As many radials as possible and as long as possible. Tie into water system.

8' copper ground rod

Fig. 23 Inexpensive vertical antenna for 80 and 160 meter operation. Top loading coil resonates antenna to 80 meters and bottom coil adds extra loading for 160 meters. Antenna is made of 20 foot length of aluminum irrigation pipe.

of white PVC plastic pipe, 1-7/8 inches (4.76 cm) in diameter. One end is filed enough to make a slip fit into the aluminum tube. A PVC plastic cap is cemented on the opposite end of the coil form.

The coil winding consists of 100 feet (30.4 m) of no. 12 enamel wire, the top end soldered to a lug attached to a threaded brazing rod which serves as a small top-loading device. The rod passes through the PVC cap and is held in place with two brass nuts and lock washers. The bottom end of the coil winding is attached to the aluminum tube with stainless steel bolts and nuts. All joints are coated with General Electric RTV-108 sealant when finished.

Supporting the Antenna

The antenna is supported by a 4 x 4 wood post sunk in the ground. The bottom end of the post is protected with a wrapping of aluminum foil, as described elsewhere in this handbook. The antenna is held to the post by means of stainless steel hose clamps.

To add strength to the support and to prevent the aluminum tube from collapsing at the clamping points, pieces of 2-3/8 inch (6 cm) outside diameter PVC are cut and slit down the middle, making a cuff to fit between the pipe and the clamp. When properly installed, guy wires are not needed.

Before the antenna is tuned, the radial system must be installed. In one instance, a ground rod is used, along with four quarter-wave radials laid atop the grass, plus four shorter radials running in random directions. The antenna is also grounded to the main water system of the residence.

Tuning the Antenna

The antenna is connected to the ground system via a two turn coil and adjusted to frequency with the aid of a dip meter. The number of turns in the top loading coil are trimmed, a turn at a time, until the antenna is resonant at the spot chosen in the 80 meter band. A protective coat of General Cement Co. "Insu-volt" varnish (G.C. 10-608) is brushed over the coil.

The next step is to install the 160 meter base coil. This consists of 40 turns of 3/16-inch (4.76 mm) diameter copper tubing wound on a 4 inch (10.2 cm) diameter form. The form is then removed and the coil threaded onto four plastic strips into which holes are drilled to separate the turns the diameter of the tubing.

The coil is connected between the base of the antenna and ground by means of heavy, flexible leads with a copper clip on the free end. Again, antenna resonance is established, this time at a spot in the 160 meter band with the use of the dip meter.

The last step is to adjust the tap point on the coil for the best SWR on the feedline. Antenna resonance and tap point are slightly interlocking and both coil taps must be moved to achieve a low value of SWR.

Antenna bandwidth on 80 meters is about 40 kHz between the 2-to-1 SWR points, and is about 15 kHz on the 160 meter band

(The original version of this antenna was described by Ed Marriner, W6XM, in the April, 1983 issue of "CQ" magazine.)

Chapter 4

Antenna Matching Devices

It is an unusual antenna that provides an exact match to a coaxial transmission line. And even when such a match is achieved at the resonant frequency of the antenna, the match can quickly deteriorate when the antenna is operated far off its design frequency.

In the case of the short vertical antenna, the feedpoint resistance is much lower than 50 ohms and its frequency response (operating bandwidth) may be quite narrow. The feedpoint resistance of a short, 160 meter coil-loaded vertical, for example, could be as low as one ohm and the feedpoint reactance could be as great as -1400 ohms. Typical resistance and reactance values for a short 160 meter vertical antenna are illustrated in Figs. 1 and 2. The problem, then, is to match such an antenna to a 50 or 75 ohm coaxial line to achieve a low value of SWR (standing wave ratio) over a reasonable operating range as required by today's modern, solid state transmitters.

The Loading Coil

Two requirements must be met for a good antenna match. First, the antenna must be resonant, or nearly so. Second, it must present a feedpoint resistance equal to the transmission line impedance. Resonance of a short antenna is established by use

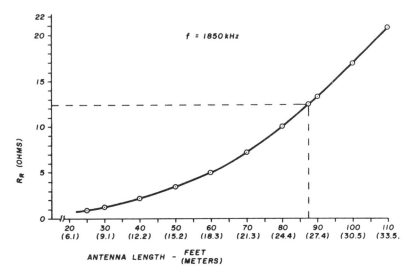

Fig. 1 Approximate feedpoint resistance (R) for a short 160 meter vertical antenna. Eighty-seven foot antenna has resistance of 12.5 ohms (neglecting ground loss).

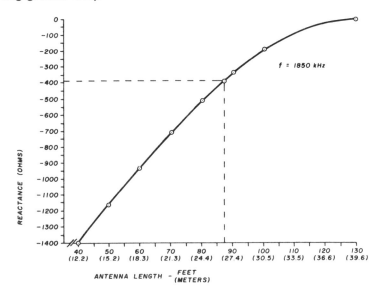

Fig. 2 Approximate feedpoint reactance for a short 160 meter vertical antenna. Eighty-seven foot antenna has reactance of -390 ohms.

of a loading coil connected in series with it as shown in chapter 3.

For good efficiency, the loading coil should have a high ratio of reactance to rf resistance. This factor is expressed in terms of coil Q. A high-Q coil is wound of heavy wire on a low loss form. The winding is often spaced the wire diameter and the length of the coil is commonly about twice the diameter.

As an example, assume a loading coil has a reactance of 1500 ohms. If the coil has a Q-factor of 300, then the rf resistance of the coil is the reactance divided by the Q, or 1500/300 = 5 ohms. If the feedpoint resistance of an antenna using this coil is 20 ohms, the overall antenna efficiency (omitting any ground loss) is 20/(20+5), or 80 percent. The remaining 20 percent of the rf power is lost as heat in the coil.

Feed Point Transformation

The feedpoint resistance of a short antenna is very low compared to a full-size one, but this value can be transformed to a higher one by means of a matching device placed in the line between the antenna and an SWR meter which monitors the degree of match. A convenient point for the match is at the base of the antenna. Some devices can establish both antenna resonance and impedance matching at the same time. Many forms of matching devices exist, and some of the useful ones are discussed in this chapter.

The Reactance Matching Technique

As shown in Figs. 1 and 2, the resonant antenna exhibits no reactance at the feedpoint, but shows positive or negative reactance when it is operated off-frequency. The reactance can be put to good use when it is desired to match the antenna to a coax line.

In most cases, the feedpoint resistance of a resonant vertical antenna falls in the range of 5 to 36 ohms, depending upon the size of the antenna relative to the operating wavelength. Very short antennas have low values of feedpoint resistance and longer antennas have higher values. The problem is to match the resistance value, whatever it is, to the transmission line.

The L-networks summarized in Fig. 3 are basic matching devices and will do the job. They require two components (an inductor and a capacitor), but it is possible to eliminate the series-connected component by letting the antenna take its place. This is accomplished by detuning (equalizing) the antenna slightly so as to introduce the correct value of series reactance at the base to compensate for the missing network component. If the antenna is made longer than the resonant length, its feedpoint reactance will be positive (inductive) and if it is shorter than resonance, the reactance will be negative (capacitive).

Using the Reactance Match

The shunt reactance to be added at the antenna feedpoint to make this system work is of the opposite sign to that of the antenna. That is, if the antenna is shorter than the resonant length (negative reactance), a shunt inductor (L) must be added (Fig. 4A). On the other hand, if the antenna is long (positive reactance), a shunt capacitor (C) is called for. (It is interesting to note that the shunt inductor scheme is used in some Yagi beams. The coil takes the form of a U-shaped inductor, or "hairpin").

This is an inexpensive and easy way to match the feedpoint resistance of a vertical antenna to a coax line. One component and a slight change of antenna length does the job!

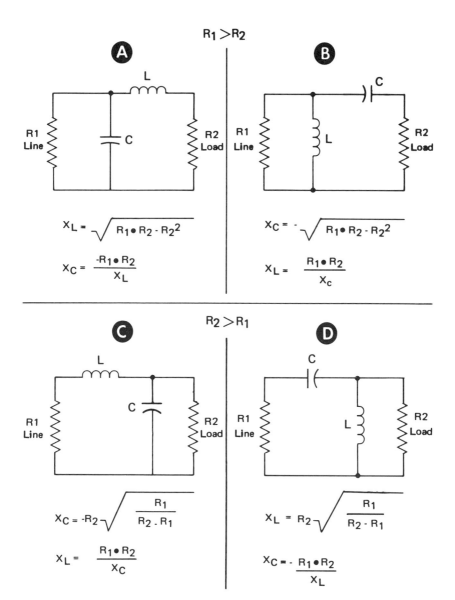

Fig. 3 Basic L-networks used to match antenna to feedline. Networks A and B are used when coax line impedance is greater than feedpoint resistance. Networks C and D are used when feedpoint resistance is greater than coax impedance.

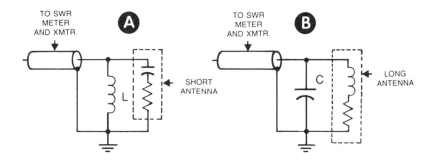

Fig. 4 Reactance of antenna shorter (A) or longer (B) than resonance can be used to simulate one of the elements of the L-network. Example A is similar to network shown in Fig. 3B. Example B is similar to Fig. 3A.

Practical Reactance Matching Circuits

The matching technique is summarized in Fig. 5. The X-axis of the graph represents the feedpoint resistance of the antenna and the Y-axis the shunt reactance necessary to achieve the match. The graph is computed for 50 ohm coax line, but the value derived is close enough for use with a 75 ohm line.

For example, assume an antenna has a feedpoint resistance of 20 ohms. The corresponding value of shunt reactance, as shown by the dashed lines on the graph, is 40 ohms. If the experimenter decides to employ a shunt coil and to equalize the antenna by shortening it, formula A is used to determine the inductance required at the antenna feedpoint. If the decision is to lengthen the antenna, a shunt capacitor is required and formula B is used to determine its value.

Representative values of shunt components are given in the table for various amateur bands. These are maximum values required for the greatest degree of mismatch between antenna and feedline.

On the higher frequency bands there is little choice between the two matching techniques. But on

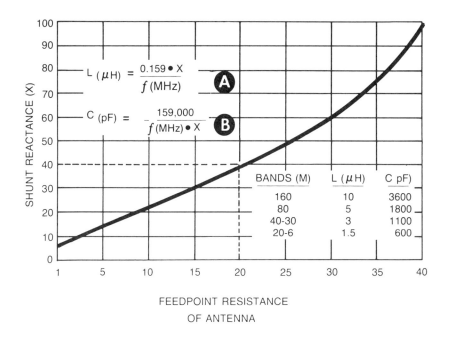

Fig. 5 The value of L-network components is given by formulas A and B. Representative component values for various amateur bands are given in the table.

the low bands, 160 meters for example, the cost of a shunt inductor is small, but the cost of a suitable large shunt capacitor might be quite high. For this reason, many amateurs prefer the inductive match system over the capacitive version.

For any band the shunt inductor can be a small, air-wound coil. In the case of the shunt capacitor, postage stamp size silver mica capacitors will suffice for power levels up to about 100 watts. Above this level, transmitting-type mica capacitors or variable air capacitors, of at least 1 kV rating, are to be preferred.

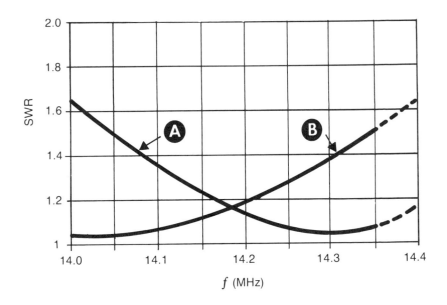

Fig. 6 Antenna resonant at 14.3 MHz (curve A) is detuned so that resonance occurs at 14.0 MHz (curve B) when impedance matching reactance is placed across feedpoint. In many cases, detuning effect is insignificant and may be ignored. Otherwise antenna element must be equalized to reestablish resonance.

Equalizing the Antenna

It was stated earlier that to make this matching system work, the antenna must be slightly detuned (equalized) to provide the necessary reactance at the feedpoint. What does this mean in practice? By definition, when an antenna is detuned from one frequency it becomes resonant at another frequency. As an example, assume that a ground plane antenna has a feedpoint resistance of 35 ohms at 14.3 MHz. It is desired to match it to a coax line. The inductance value is determined from Fig. 5, formula A, and the coil is placed across the feedpoint. An SWR plot of antenna response is run across the 20 meter band and compared with the plot run before the inductor was added (Fig. 6). Now the antenna is resonant at 14.0 MHz. It should be shortened enough to move the resonant frequency back to 14.3 MHz.

But is this equalization necessary? The antenna theorist may decide to shorten his antenna to restore the original SWR response curve but the realist knows that the new antenna response curve is equally satisfactory and doesn't want to waste the time and effort to equalize the antenna. He knows the "station at the other end" won't know the difference!

The owner of a solid-state transmitter, on the other hand, may require antenna equalization because he discovers that he cannot properly load his transmitter at the end of the band where the transmission line SWR is excessive. He has the choice of equalizing his antenna, or incorporating a matching device (L-network) in the line at his transmitter to accomplish a satisfactory match.

To sum it up, the amount of antenna equalization required for the matching system to work depends upon the ratio of the antenna feedpoint resistance to the coax line impedance. The greater the ratio, the more equalization required. The example given shows that for a feedpoint resistance close in value to the coax impedance equalization probably is inconsequential, as the detuning effect of the match isn't very great. If, on the other hand, the effect is enough to move the antenna resonant frequency out of the amateur band, equalization is called for.

In the case of a very short vertical (a mobile whip, for example) equalization is necessary. A test run on an 8-foot (2.44 m), center-loaded 80 meter whip antenna having a feedpoint resistance of about 5 ohms showed that the inductance of the loading coil had to be changed about fifteen percent to provide a good match to a 50 ohm line at the design frequency after a matching capacitor was added.

In this instance, the easiest solution was to leave the loading coil alone and to add series inductance at the base of the antenna to equalize it at the operating frequency.

The L-Network

Another solution to the antenna matching problem is the L-network. This device can achieve antenna resonance and establish a match at the same time. It is adjustable over a large range and can be tuned to hold the SWR to near-unity when a frequency change is made.

Two components are used in the L-network and they can be connected in four possible combinations so as to provide either a step down or a step up match, as shown in Fig. 3. Illustrations A and B show two step down networks where the load (R2) is less in value than the feedpoint (R1). In most cases, R1 is the coax feedline impedance (50 or 75 ohms) and R2 is the feedpoint resistance of the antenna (less than 50 ohms). Either network will do the job and the user makes his choice depending upon whether he wishes series or shunt inductance or capacitance. The choice is often made on an economic basis--the cost of the components. It must be kept in mind, however, that the A-type network provides some degree of harmonic attenuation and that the B-type does not.

Figures 3C and D show two step up networks where the load (R2) is greater than the feedpoint impedance (R1). These networks are the reverse image of those shown in illustration A and B. The C-type network provides some harmonic attenuation.

Using the L-network

The basis of the L-network is the fact that for any circuit consisting of a resistance and a reactance in series (an antenna for example), there

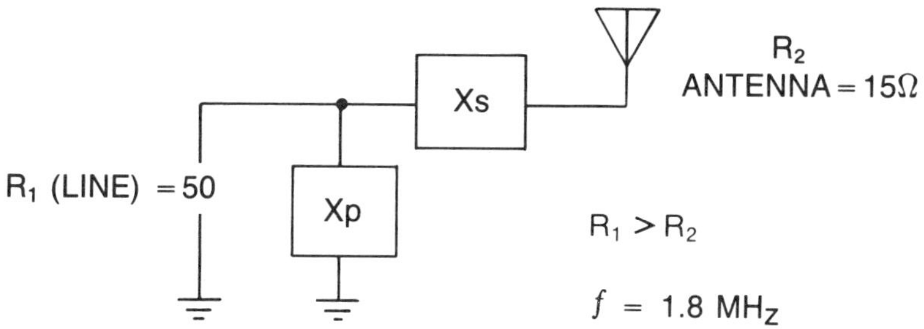

$R_1 \text{ (LINE)} = 50$

R_2
$\text{ANTENNA} = 15\Omega$

$R_1 > R_2$

$f = 1.8 \text{ MH}_Z$

(1) $X_S = \sqrt{R_1 \cdot R_2 - R_2^2} = \sqrt{750 - 225} = 22.92\Omega$

(2) $X_p = \dfrac{R_1 \cdot R_2}{X_S} = \dfrac{750}{22.92} = 32.72\Omega$

(3) $L = \dfrac{0.159 \cdot X_L}{f \text{ (MH}_Z)} \quad (\mu H)$

(4) $C = \dfrac{159,000}{f \text{ (MH}_Z) \cdot X_C} \quad (pF)$

CHOICE No. 1: Let X_S be inductive and X_p be capacitive.

$X_S = \dfrac{0.159 \times 22.92}{1.8} = 2.02 \, \mu H$

$X_p = \dfrac{159,000}{1.8 \times 32.72} = 2699.5 \text{ pF}$

CHOICE No. 2: Let X_S = be capacitive and Xp be inductive.

$X_S = \dfrac{159,000}{1.8 \times 22.72} = 3853.6 \text{ pF}$

$X_p = \dfrac{0.159 \times 32.72}{1.8} = 2.89 \, \mu H$

Fig. 7 L-network summary. General case is shown for series (Xs) and parallel (Xp) components. Formulas 1-4 provide component values in picofarads and microhenries when frequency is expressed in megahertz. Example of two choices is given for network types A and B, Fig. 3.

exists an equivalent circuit consisting of resistance and reactance in parallel that has the same electrical characteristics (but different component values) for a given frequency (Fig. 7). This generalized example provides an impedance step down transformation and is useful to match a 50 or 75 ohm coax line to a resonant antenna whose feedpoint resistance is less than the line value.

The illustration shows a 160 meter antenna with a feedpoint resistance of 15 ohms to be matched to a 50 ohm transmission line. Formulas 1 and 2 show that the series network reactance (Xs) has a value of 22.92 ohms and the value of the parallel reactance (Xp) is 32.72 ohms.

The network user has the choice of making either reactance an inductor or a capacitor so long as one is the reverse of the other. Formulas 1-4 summarizes the two choices. At the design frequency (1.8 MHz, for example), the circuits are electrically equivalent. The choice of circuits is usually made based upon the size, cost and availability of the components. If, for example, Xs is chosen to be an inductor, it will have a value of 2.02 uH. Then Xp must be a capacitor and it will have a value of 2699.5 pF (choice #1). This amounts to a very small coil and a rather large capacitor. The series coil can be removed and replaced by the inductive reactance of a longer-than-resonance antenna.

The reverse choice (#2) shows comparable component values. The series capacitor has a value of 3853.6 pF and the shunt inductor has a value of 2.89 uH. The series capacitor (Xs) can be removed from the network circuit and its place taken by the capacitive reactance of a shorter-than-resonance antenna. The capacitor costs nothing and the shunt coil is inexpensive and very small in size. An ideal combination! This technique is used in the antenna shown in Chapter 3, Fig. 4.

Fig. 8 L-network for 160 meters. Shunt capacitor is made up of large value air variable unit plus shunt-connected mica transmitting units. Rotary coil is large enough to take care of additional series loading inductance required by short Marconi antenna (see Fig. 9). Components are mounted on plywood base with fiberboard panel. Counter dial is coupled to rotary inductor.

The Shunt Capacitor L-Network

A versatile network is shown in Figs. 8 and 9. It is an A-type network (Fig. 3) employing a shunt variable capacitor and a series rotary inductor. Values of the components depend upon the band of use and the antenna impedance to be matched.

This network is designed to match a short antenna on the 160 and 80 meter bands and, as a result, the component values are quite large. For 160 meters, the shunt capacitor is made up of two .0011 mF

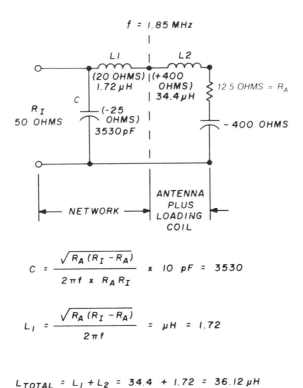

$$C = \frac{\sqrt{R_A (R_I - R_A)}}{2\pi f \times R_A R_I} \times 10 \text{ pF} = 3530$$

$$L_I = \frac{\sqrt{R_A (R_I - R_A)}}{2\pi f} = \mu H = 1.72$$

$$L_{TOTAL} = L_I + L_2 = 34.4 + 1.72 = 36.12 \mu H$$

Fig. 9 Schematic of L-network. 36 uH inductor is used. Total parallel capacitance is about 3530 pF. "Worst case" antenna has feedpoint resistance of 12.5 ohms with capacitive reactance of about -390 ohms (see Figs. 1 and 2).

transmitting-type mica capacitors in parallel with a 2000 pF, transmitting-type variable air capacitor. The inductor is an 18 uH rotary coil. (Johnson type 229-0202-01, or equivalent). Extra additional inductance can be conected in series with the coil if required for a very short antenna. Short antennas having input resistances as low as 10 ohms can be matched to 50 ohms with this device. In addition, the rotary inductor can compensate for antenna reactance.

The unit is built on a plywood base with a Masonite panel. The inductor is driven by a counter dial to provide accurate logging. A coaxial receptacle is mounted on a small L-shaped metal bracket at the rear of the assembly. The shell of the receptacle is connected to the rotor terminal of the variable capacitor and to a ground post at the rear of the network.

Tuning the L-Network

The network is placed at the transmitter, after the SWR meter. For initial tuneup, the transmitter is run at reduced power and the network controls adjusted for a minimum reverse reading on the SWR meter. As the SWR reading is reduced, transmitter power is increased until full input is run when the SWR reaches unity (1-to-1).

After initial adjustments are made, the network dial readings are logged for various frequencies across the band so that the network can be quickly retuned when a frequency change is made.

It is a good idea to run a separate ground lead between the network and the transmitter and not rely upon the shield of the interconnecting coax line to do the job. An external radio ground connection is made to the ground terminal of the network.

The Step Up Network

Multiwire Marconi and extended, base-fed antennas having a high value of feedpoint resistance require a network that that will step 50 ohms up to that value. An L-network in reverse will do the job. Component values for a particular network design can be derived from the formulas given in Figs. 3C and D if the feedpoint resistance of the antenna is known.

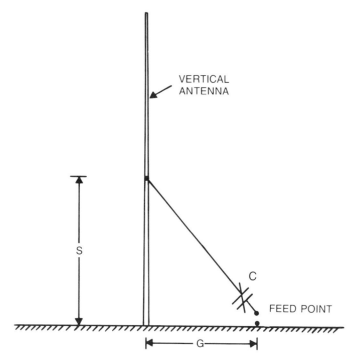

Fig. 10 The shunt-fed antenna. Vertical tower is excited by feeder wire tapped at point S. Capacitor tunes out reactance of wire. Feed wire can also be brought down parallel to the antenna. This system is often used to shunt-feed an existing tower which supports a hf or vhf antenna.

The Shunt-fed Antenna

The vertical antenna can be grounded at the base and power applied across a section of it (S), as shown in Fig. 10. This idea can be considered as an antenna in which the power is applied between the grounded end and a tap point which, in conjunction with the feed wire and the ground return path (G), form a one-turn loop. The reactive component of the loop, which is inductive, is resonated out by means of a series-connected capacitor (C). The point at which the feed wire is connected to the antenna depends upon the height, diameter and taper of the antenna, and wire spacing from it. The distance (S) varies from 20 to 50 percent of the antenna height. The feed wire can be sloped away from the antenna, or brought down parallel to it to a suitable termination point.

The performance of a shunt-fed antenna is substantially the same as one with conventional series feed, provided the resistance of the ground return path (G) is low.

Unloaded vertical antennas as short as 0.15 wavelength may be shunt-fed. Below this length, the tap point of the feed wire may be higher than the physical height of the antenna.

The Shunt-fed Tower

A grounded metal tower used to support a beam or other antenna may be shunt-fed for low band operation. The "gamma match" is commonly used for this purpose. This consists of a single rod or wire parallel to the tower and attached to it at the far end (Fig. 11). It is resonated by a series capacitor at the feedpoint. Length and spacing of the rod from the tower and the ratio of rod diameter to tower cross-section determines the dimensions of the system. Test results of shunt feeding towers of various heights for 40 meter operation are shown in Fig. 12. These tests were run by John True, W4OQ, and are summarized in the May, 1975 issue of "Ham Radio" magazine. Gamma match dimensions are given for towers whose height range from 24 to 90 feet (7.3 to 27.4 m). The test tower was 20 inches (51 cm) on a side and spacing of the gamma rod from one tower leg was 10 inches (25.5 cm). The parallel connected capacitor permits fine adjustment to compensate for changes in gamma rod length.

If the gamma rod is shorter than optimum or the tower-to-gamma spacing too small, adjustment of this

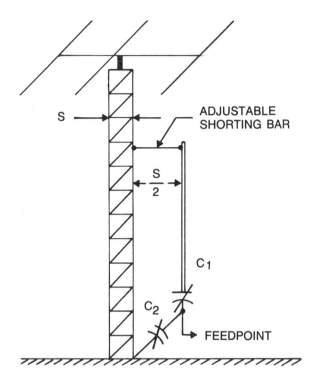

Fig. 11 Shunt-fed tower uses beam antenna for top loading effect. (See Chapter 3, Fig. 18 for loading data.) Gamma rod is spaced half the tower width from one vertical member. Top of rod is shorted to tower by means of adjustable metal strap. Series capacitor (C1) tunes gamma device to resonance and shunt capacitor (C2) permits fine adjustment to compensate for changes in gamma rod length.

capacitor simplifies the task of setting the shorting bar between the rod and the tower.

Note that at the near-resonant length of the tower (about 34 feet, or 10.4 m), the length of the gamma rod is minimum and the series capacitor value is maximum. Below a tower height of 24 feet (7.3 m or about 0.17 wavelength) the value of the series capacitor approaches a minimum and the length of the gamma rod approaches the height of the tower. This is the limiting case.

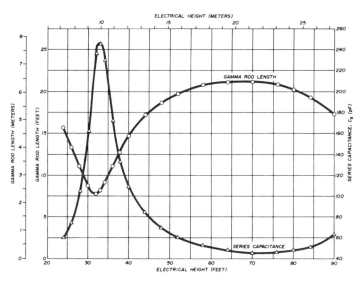

Fig. 12 40-meter vertical. Gamma rod length and series capacitance vs. electrical height of tower. Parallel capacitance required to match coax line is approximately 325 pF.

Fig 13 80-meter vertical. Gamma rod length and series capacitor vs. electrical height of tower. Parallel capacitance required to match coax line is approximately 650 pF.

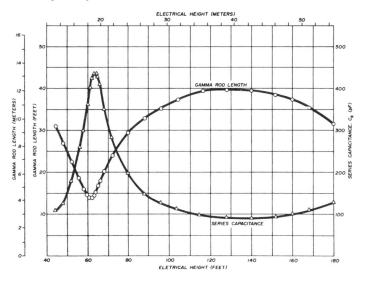

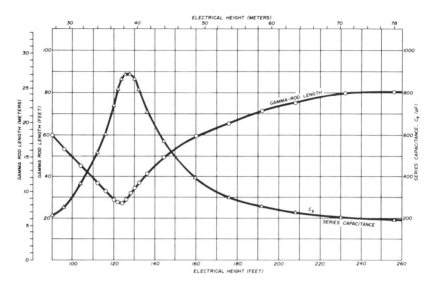

Fig. 14 160-meter vertical. Gamma rod length and series capacitor vs electrical height of tower. Parallel capacitance required to match coax line is approximately 1300 pF.

Gamma Match Construction

A rugged assembly can be made by constructing the gamma rod of one inch (25 mm) diameter aluminum tubing spaced away from the tower 10 to 20 inches (25 to 50 cm), depending upon the cross-section size of the tower. If difficulty is experienced in matching, the rod-to-tower spacing should be changed.

The rod can be spaced from the tower by means of insulators made of one inch PVC plastic water pipe. One end of each insulator is notched to fit the tower leg. Slots are cut in the pipe on each side of the end and a hose clamp is run through the slots and around the tower leg. A similar arrangement is used for the gamma rod (Fig. 15). The variable shorting bar is made of aluminum strap connected between the rod and the tower by means of hose clamps.

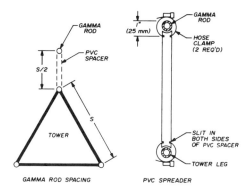

Fig. 15 Construction of gamma rod matching system. Spacers are made from PVC water pipe with ends slotted to pass hose clamps which encircle tower legs.

Small receiving-size variable capacitors can be used for the gamma match for power levels up to 150 watts, but transmitting capacitors with a plate spacing of about 0.15 inch (3.8 mm), or more, should be used for power up to the legal limit. It is important that both capacitors be protected from the weather by placing them in a waterproof box.

Adjusting the Gamma Match

Length and diameter of the gamma rod, the spacing from the tower, and the value of the capacitors determine the impedance transformation. A dip meter and the rf impedance bridge described in a later chapter can be used to adjust the match. The feedpoint of the gamma match is attached to the terminals of the bridge. In brief, a small amount of rf power is fed to the match and dip meter. Frequency, gamma capacitance and rod length are varied until a null is found at a bridge setting of 50 ohms. If it is difficult to find a null, the rod-to-tower spacing should be increased. Once a preliminary null has been found, the various component dimensions are refined to position the null at the design frequency of the antenna. The matching system is rather broad in adjustment and can move the resonant frequency of the tower several hundred kHz to complete the match.

Preparing the Tower

The tower must be prepared to work properly as a vertical antenna. Metallic guy wires should be broken up by strain insulators every 10 feet (3 m). All control cables and coaxial leads coming down the tower should be taped to one leg of the tower and run down to ground level. They are then brought away from the tower on the surface of the ground, or under the ground, suitably protected.

If the tower is the crank-up type, jumpers should be connected across the joints to insure a good electrical connection between the tower sections.

Since the tower is only one-half of the antenna system, care must be taken to install an efficient radio ground system. In addition, the tower should be grounded against lightning by one or two ground rods at the base. A system of radial wires laid out on, or above, the surface of the ground will suffice for proper operation of the tower as a vertical antenna. See chapter 2 for additional details.

The Matching Device--The Final Word

A matching device can match the feedpoint resistance of any vertical antenna to a coax transmission line. The device can take the form of an L-network, or a linear network such as a gamma match. In addition to impedance transformation, the L-network can also establish resonance in many cases. The gamma match, in particular, is useful in matching an existing tower for service as a vertical antenna.

Chapter 5

Ground Plane Antennas

One of the most popular antennas for both hf and vhf service is the ground plane antenna. The basic design is a quarter-wavelength vertical antenna mounted above horizontal, one-quarter wavelength radials spaced equidistant around the antenna base (see Chap. 2, Fig. 11). The antenna radiates an omnidirectional, vertically polarized pattern.

The radiation resistance of a full-size ground plane antenna runs between 35 and 50 ohms (depending upon radial placement) and provides a good match to a coaxial transmission line.

The radials provide a radio (rf) ground point directly below the antenna and when the ground plane is mounted a half-wavelength or more above the surface of the earth, ground return current losses are quite low. The theoretical field strength of a ground plane is about 0.8 dB less than an equivalent dipole but in real-life the two antennas show equal performance.

When mounted in the clear above good ground the ground plane antenna provides low angle radiation that is necessary for long distance communication.

Shown in this chapter are various ground plane antenna designs for the hf and vhf bands that are useful for general amateur service. Information is provided for use of the antennas at any frequency in the hf spectrum.

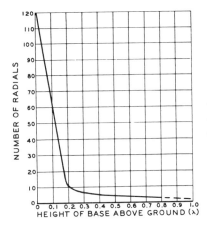

Fig. 1 As base of vertical antenna is elevated above ground fewer radials are required until, when base is about one-half wave in the air, only 3 or 4 radials are necessary.

How Many Radials are Needed?

The vhf ground plane antenna mounted several wavelengths above the earth works well with only three or four radials, equally spaced around the base of the antenna, provided the feedline is isolated from the antenna field. It has been shown, however, that when the antenna is close to the ground in terms of wavelength, more radials are required because the vertically polarized field of the antenna is susceptible to ground losses below, and in the immediate vicinity of, the antenna. A hf ground plane close to the earth (that is, with the base on the ground or less than 0.1 wavelength above it) may require from 60 to 120 radials to effectively shield the antenna from the "lossy" ground. As the ground plane is raised in the air, fewer and fewer radials are required for good performance until, when the base of the antenna is about one-half wavelength (or more) in the air, the number of radials can be reduced to three or four without incurring severe ground loss (Fig. 1).

For example, for a rooftop installation of a 20 meter ground plane on a single story residence, with the base of the antenna about 10 to 15 feet (3 to 4.5 m) above the surrounding ground level, a minimum

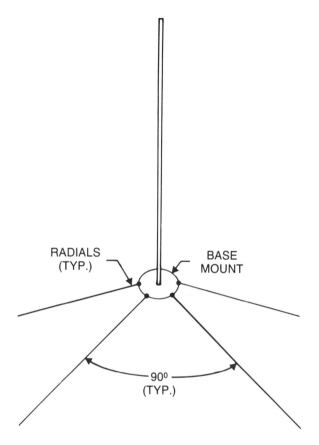

Fig. 2 When radials slope downward about 40 degrees from the horizontal the feedpoint resistance of the ground plane antenna rises to 50 ohms.

of 6 radials is suggested. On the other hand, if the same antenna is mounted atop a house or tower with the base about one-half wavelength, or 35 feet (10.6 m) above ground, only three or four radials are required to provide good performance.

"Drooping" Radials

The classic ground plane design places all radials in the horizontal plane, equally spaced

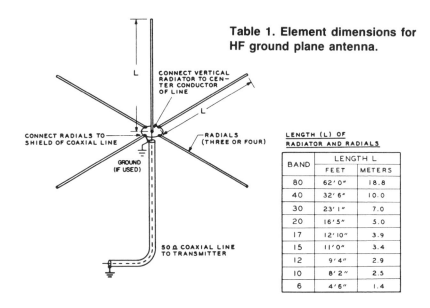

Table 1. Element dimensions for HF ground plane antenna.

LENGTH (L) OF RADIATOR AND RADIALS

BAND	LENGTH L	
	FEET	METERS
80	62' 0"	18.8
40	32' 6"	10.0
30	23' 1"	7.0
20	16' 5"	5.0
17	12' 10"	3.9
15	11' 0"	3.4
12	9' 4"	2.9
10	8' 2"	2.5
6	4' 6"	1.4

around the antenna base. This provides the best approximation of a solid ground plane. It is possible, however, to slope the radials downwards from the horizontal plane. This causes them to radiate and thus raises the feedpoint resistance of the antenna. A downward slope of about 40 degrees from the horizontal raises the feedpoint resistance of the antenna to about 50 ohms, providing a good match for a coaxial line. When this is done, the radials can also serve as guy wires for the antenna (Fig. 2).

When the radials droop down as shown, the gain of the ground plane is raised by about 0.3 dB over that of the normal configuration, but the protection of the near-field from ground loss is reduced. It is doubtful if a casual observer listening to a signal transmitted first by a conventional ground plane and then by a "drooping" version could notice any difference in signal strength.

Practical Ground Plane Antennas for the HF Bands

The ground plane antenna is a popular performer on the hf bands. It is too large, however, for the lower frequency bands unless the user has plenty of space for the radial system. On the higher bands (10-50 MHz) it is small enough to fit into many small back or side yards. One common design takes the form of a vertical aluminum radiator attached to a wood mounting post, or a house chimney, with a network of ground plane wires at the base. A completely self-supporting installation can be made which utilizes aluminum tubing for the radials.

If the ground plane antenna is clear of the ground (say, 0.2 wavelength), a minimum of six radials is recommended. Many amateur installations use up to ten or twenty radials, as they are inexpensive to install and relatively unobtrusive. At higher antenna elevations, less radials are required.

Antenna dimensions for the high frequency bands are given in Table 1 along with the general formula for ground plane dimensions for frequencies up to 50 MHz. Antenna and radial lengths are the same.

The dimensions are for wire or tubing elements less than 0.5 inch (12.7 mm) in diameter. For larger diameter elements, the lengths should be multiplied by 0.98.

Tapered elements are a special case. In this instance, the tapered element is longer than normal. The amount of correction depends upon the ratio of the base-to-tip diameter of the element. For a ratio of 2, the lengths given are multiplied by 1.02; for a ratio of 3, by 1.04;and for a ratio of 4, by 1.06.

Erecting a Ground Plane Antenna

The easiest approach is to buy a kit antenna from a reputable manufacturer. Amateurs interested in 10 or 6 meter operation can often purchase an 11 meter

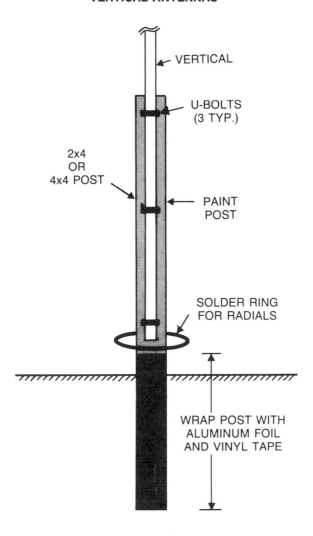

Fig. 3 Ground post to support vertical antenna is made waterproof at base by a heavy multiple wrapping of overlapping aluminum foil held in place with vinyl tape.

CB ground plane antenna and cut it to frequency. For the lower frequency bands, however, it usually is less expensive to build the antenna than to buy a kit. The vertical section can be made of telescoping aluminum tubing (normally available at the larger hardware stores and metal dealers) and the radials of copper wire.

If the base of the antenna is near ground level, a wood post can be sunk into the ground and the antenna mounted on it. A practical ground-mounted antenna is shown in Fig.3. The base of the post is well painted and wrapped with several layers of overlapping, kitchen-type heavy aluminum foil to protect it from termites, damp earth, and ground water. The wrapping is carried up the post to above ground level and is held in place by vinyl electrical tape. If the antenna is guyed, the post need be sunk in the ground only two or three feet (0.6 to 0.9 m). An unguyed antenna requires a longer ground post.

Since the rf voltage at the base of the ground plane antenna is relatively low, the post is given several preservative coats of roofing compound or varnish and the antenna bolted directly to it by means of TV-type, galvanized U-bolts.

The radials can be soldered to a ring of bare copper wire circling the post directly under the antenna. The ring is connected to the shield of the coax line. Since the far ends of the radials are "hot" with rf, they are attached to insulators which are held in position by short lengths of rope or wire.

The technique of attaching the coaxial line to the wire ring is very important so as not to allow water to enter the line. In a heavy rainstorm, a goodly amount of water runs down the vertical to the base and unless precautions are taken, the water enters the coaxial line and is sucked along the inside of the line by capillary action of the braided, outer shield. Line deterioration and increased rf losses will quickly follow if this comes to pass.

Protecting the Line

There are several ways of protecting the coax line from moisture. One of the best is to place a waterproof coaxial connector on the line and a matching receptacle at the antenna base. The popular type PL-259 plug and SO-239 receptacle are not waterproof and are not recommended for the job, although a number of amateurs use them.

If you do use these connectors, screw them on very tightly, tape every joint with vinyl electrical tape, or the newer electrical sealing tape, and then coat everything with General Electric RTV-108 sealant.

The modern type-N coax connectors are waterproof, however, and can be used, provided the user has the expertise to place the plug on the line correctly (Fig. 4).

The next best bet is to peel the outer insulation of the line back for a few inches, unbraid the shield and twist it into a pig-tail connection. The inner insulation is then stripped back from the center conductor for an inch or so. Connections can be made to these terminals. In order to waterproof the joint, it is coated with a sealant (General Electric RTV-108, for example) and then wrapped with vinyl electric tape.

The VHF Ground Plane Antenna

The ground plane is an extremely popular antenna on the amateur bands above 10 meters. The greater percentage of fm repeater operation employs vertical polarization because of the mobiles that use the repeaters. Remarks that apply to the high frequency ground plane antenna apply equally to the vhf ground

N

ASSEMBLY
INSTRUCTIONS

STANDARD CLAMP

| NUT | WASHER SPREAD | GASKET | CLAMP | FEMALE CONTACT | JACK BODY | MALE CONTACT | PLUG BODY |

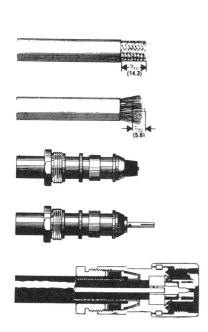

Remove ⁹⁄₁₆″(14.3mm) of vinyl jacket. When using double shielded cable, remove ⅝″(15.9mm).

Comb out copper braid as shown. Cut off dielectric ⁷⁄₃₂″(5.6) from end. Tin center conductor.

Taper braid as shown. Slide nut, washer and gasket over vinyl jacket. Slide clamp over braid with internal shoulder of clamp flush against end of vinyl jacket. When assembling connectors with gland, be sure knife edge is toward end of cable and groove in gasket is toward the gland.

Smooth braid back over clamp and trim. Soft solder contact to center conductor. Avoid use of excessive heat and solder. See that end of dielectric is clean. Contact must be flush against dielectric. Outside of contact must be free of solder.

Slide body into place carefully so that contact enters hole in insulator. Face of dielectric must be flush against insulator. Slide completed assembly into body by pushing nut. When nut is in place, tighten with wrenches. In connectors with gland, knife-edge should cut gasket in half by tightening sufficiently.

NOTE: For armored cable slide cap over armor first. Push armor and cap back out of way and proceed with assembly as directed above using armor clamp in place of standard clamp nut. When assembly is complete straighten bulge in armor and trim so it can be clamped between nut and cap.

Fig. 4 Amphenol instructions for assembly of type-N waterproof coaxial fitting. Type UG-21/U plug is used. (Drawing courtesy Amphenol Corp.)

f (MHz)	Element Length
	Inches (CM)
144.0	19.50 (49.5)
146.0	19.25 (19.25)
223.0	12.60 (32.0)
445.0	6.30 (16.00)

Table 2. Element dimensions for VHF ground plane antenna.

$$\text{LENGTH (IN)} = \frac{2808}{f \text{ (MHz)}}$$

plane, with the exception that the vhf antenna is usually mounted many wavelengths above ground. This helps to counteract ground loss beneath the antenna, but complicates matters in that it is easy for the field of the antenna to interact with the outer shield of the coaxial transmission line unless precautions are taken during the installation of the antenna. Interaction such as this causes the line to become part of the antenna and tends to nullify the good, low angle radiation of the antenna, making it less useful for vhf ground range coverage.

Building the VHF Ground Plane Antenna

As mentioned earlier, several manufacturers provide antenna kits and it is economical to purchase one, as the kit often costs less than the equivalent aluminum and hardware required to build the antenna. Antenna dimensions specified with the kit can be matched against the information given in this chapter.

In the region above 30 MHz, the diameter of the conductors used in the ground plane antenna becomes of importance because this dimension starts to approximate a fraction of a wavelength. As the element length-to-diameter ratio decreases, the element becomes shorter for a given frequency. That is to say, a "fat" element is shorter than a "thin" one. This distinction is relatively unimportant below 30 MHz for simple antennas but assumes greater significance as the higher frequencies are approached.

Table 2 provides element dimensions for ground plane antennas for use in the vhf/uhf spectrum. Generally speaking, it is best to use "thin" elements. One-quarter inch (6.35 mm) diameter tubing is suggested for the 144 MHz band and one-eighth inch (3.18 mm) diameter rod or tubing is recommended for the 220 and 445 MHz bands.

Decoupling the Antenna from the Transmission Line

It is important to make sure that the field of the antenna does not influence the transmission line. In particular, the outside of the coaxial line can have rf voltage induced on it by virtue of unwanted coupling to the antenna. If coupled voltage exists, the line becomes a portion of the antenna and any SWR measurements made on the antenna are in error because the instrument "sees" the line as part of the antenna.

In addition, the interplay of radio energy between antenna and the outer shield of the line tends to distort the radiation pattern of the antenna, negating some of the low angle radiation so important on the very high frequencies.

It is simple to decouple the line from the antenna. All that is required is that the line be wound into a simple decoupling choke at a point directly below the antenna. In addition, the line should drop down directly below the antenna for at least a half-wavelength before being led off to the station.

The Decoupling Choke

A coaxial line can be wound into a circle whose diameter is about twenty times the diameter of the cable. A bend sharper than this can distort the

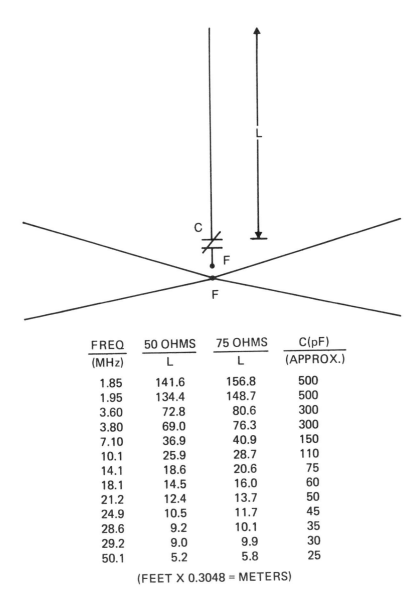

FREQ (MHz)	50 OHMS L	75 OHMS L	C(pF) (APPROX.)
1.85	141.6	156.8	500
1.95	134.4	148.7	500
3.60	72.8	80.6	300
3.80	69.0	76.3	300
7.10	36.9	40.9	150
10.1	25.9	28.7	110
14.1	18.6	20.6	75
18.1	14.5	16.0	60
21.2	12.4	13.7	50
24.9	10.5	11.7	45
28.6	9.2	10.1	35
29.2	9.0	9.9	30
50.1	5.2	5.8	25

(FEET X 0.3048 = METERS)

Fig. 5 The extended HF ground plane antenna provides good match to 50 or 75 ohm line. Series capacitor tunes out inductive reactance of antenna.

inner conductor of the cable and lead to trouble. Guided by this limitation, it is safe to wind the RG-8/U (RG-213/U)-type cable into a coil about 10 inches (25 cm) in diameter. The smaller RG-58/U-type cable can be wound into a coil approximately 5 inches (13 cm) in diameter.

A hf decoupling choke consists of six turns of cable and a vhf choke can be made from three turns of cable. The choke is held in position by means of plastic cable ties or vinyl tape. It is placed near the feedpoint of the antenna, at right angles to the plane of the radials.

The Extended HF Ground Plane Antenna

As in the case of the Marconi antenna, the length of the vertical portion of a ground plane antenna can be extended so as to raise the feedpoint resistance up to 50 or 75 ohms. In either case, radial length remains as shown in Table 1.

Dimensions for 0.28 and 0.31 wavelength long extended ground plane antennas are given in Fig. 5. The first design provides a close match to a 50 ohm coax line and the second to a 75 ohm line. Both designs require a series capacitor to establish antenna resonance. The capacitor is adjusted for lowest SWR on the line from antenna to transmitter. The capacitor is isolated from ground and placed in a waterproof box at the base of the antenna. The coaxial line is sealed against moisture at the point it enters the box.

The antenna is adjusted at the design frequency for unity SWR on the transmission line by varying the capacitor and the antenna length. Element diameter and taper data dicussed with reference to Table 1 also apply to Fig. 5.

The 5/8-wave Ground Plane Antenna

In the "Proceedings of the IRE", April, 1935 Gihring and Brown published their classic study on the field pattern along the ground for vertical antennas of different lengths. One of the results of this study has been the popularity of the 5/8-wave high vertical antenna for broadcast service and amateur VHF use. This design combined high radiation efficiency with a power gain at low radiation angles of nearly 3 dB over a comparison 1/4-wave vertical antenna. In order to establish resonance, a small base loading coil is added to the antenna to extend the electrical length to the next resonant point at 3/4 wavelength.

Amateurs have used this interesting antenna on the hf and vhf bands with mixed results. When an elaborate ground system is used, the antenna performs as expected. However, when used with conventional quarter-wave radials (as is commonly done on the vhf bands) the antenna often proves to be a disappointment, showing little, if any, power gain over a conventional ground plane antenna.

The Expanded VHF Ground Plane Antenna

Tests run by Ralph Turner, W8HXC, and Don Norman, AF8B, on various 2 meter vertical antennas have shown that under some circumstances (particularly when the antenna is many wavelengths above ground and the coax line is long in terms of wavelength) the feedline becomes part of the antenna system, in spite of the use of conventional radials. This disturbs the antenna pattern and destroys much of the low angle radiation.

The quarter-wave ground plane provides good feedline isolation if the coax line is wrapped into a decoupling coil below the antenna, as described earlier in this chapter. The 5/8-wave antenna, however, exhibits current flowing along the outside of the coax line even after it is coiled into a decoupling coil. The radials are not doing the job they were intended to do.

The 3/4-wavelength Radial System

Experiments were run on a 5/8-wave 2 meter extended ground plane antenna to determine if the feedline requires additional decoupling from the antenna field. It was found that satisfactory isolation can be obtained if the radials are lengthened to 3/4 wavelength. An antenna modified in this fashion provided superior performance over a 1/4-wave ground plane and also over a 5/8-wave ground plane with conventional 1/4-wave radials.

Extended radials on this antenna type also proved helpful during antenna tests on the 6 and 10 meter bands. It is doubtful if they would be an asset for lower frequency antennas, as these are usually mounted closer to the ground in terms of operating wavelength.

Antenna Dimensions

The expanded 5/8-wave ground plane is a large antenna when compared to the conventional 1/4-wave design and is not commonly used on the high frequency bands. It is useful in the vhf region because it is relatively small and provides power gain for omnidirectional repeater service. Shown in Fig. 6 are antenna dimensions for 28 through 440 MHz, with additional data provided for construction of the antenna for any frequencies outside the amateur assignments.

The Base Coil Adjustment

In order to establish resonance for a 5/8 wavelength antenna a small inductor is placed at the

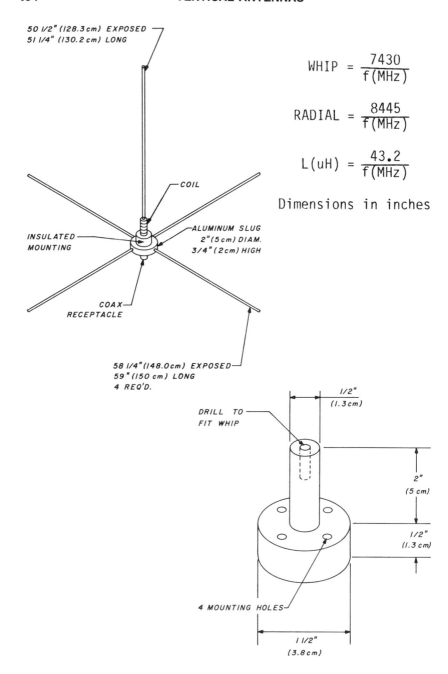

50 1/2" (128.3 cm) EXPOSED
51 1/4" (130.2 cm) LONG

$$WHIP = \frac{7430}{f(MHz)}$$

$$RADIAL = \frac{8445}{f(MHz)}$$

$$L(uH) = \frac{43.2}{f(MHz)}$$

Dimensions in inches

COIL

INSULATED MOUNTING

ALUMINUM SLUG
2" (5 cm) DIAM.
3/4" (2 cm) HIGH

COAX RECEPTACLE

58 1/4" (148.0 cm) EXPOSED
59" (150 cm) LONG
4 REQ'D.

1/2"
(1.3 cm)

DRILL TO FIT WHIP

2"
(5 cm)

1/2"
(1.3 cm)

4 MOUNTING HOLES

1 1/2"
(3.8 cm)

BAND	WHIP		RADIALS		COIL
(MHz)	IN.	CM	IN.	CM	(μ H)
28	259.00	658	294.0	746.0	1.54
50	147.6	375	167.8	426.0	0.86
144	51.25	130.2	58.25	148.0	0.30
220	33.54	85.2	38.12	96.8	0.19
440	16.77	42.6	19.1	48.5	0.09

Fig 6 The expanded 5/8-wave ground plane for 144 MHz band. Lower drawing shows mount for whip antenna. Mount is made of plastic or other insulating material.

✶   ✶   ✶   ✶

base of the antenna. A tap point on the coil near the ground end is selected and the antenna is placed in a clear position, with the base about head height.

A SWR vs. frequency curve is run and the readings logged every 50 or 100 kHz across the band. The point of lowest SWR is near the resonant frequency of the antenna. The SWR response is quite broad and the slope of the curve is very mild, showing the antenna has good bandwidth performance. Adding or subtracting a fraction of a turn from the base coil, or changing antenna length an inch or two will move the SWR minimum point to the design frequency.

The final step is to adjust the tap point, a quarter-turn at a time to reach the point of lowest SWR. The experimenter will find that coil tap, number of coil turns and vertical antenna height are interlocking. If the antenna is too short, for example, increasing coil inductance or antenna height brings it into resonance. Moving the coil tap, too, accomplishes the same purpose, although

too big a tap movement raises the SWR. The builder
will find, however, that the antenna is very
"forgiving" and adjustments are not critical.

The Radials

For vhf service, the radials can be made of small
diameter aluminum tubing. For a hf antenna, it is
recommended that the radials be made out of wire as
they are less visible (and less objectionable to
neighbors) than are the tubing equivalents.

The HF 5/8-wave Ground Plane

The 5/8-wave ground plane is an interesting
antenna for those amateurs who desire signal gain,
but do not have the room or the permission to erect
a rotary beam. This antenna provides a solid 3 dB
gain over the conventional ground plane and, when
properly installed, provides that gain at the lower
angles of radiation where it is needed for DX
contacts.

Because the feedpoint of this antenna provides a
reactive load to the transmission line, the antenna
is electrically extended to 3/4-wavelength by means
of a base loading coil.

It is possible to achieve the same match by
lengthening the antenna to 3/4-wavelength, but this
length would exhibit lobe splitting in the vertical
plane, and most of the low angle radiation would be
lost. The solution is to wind the required length
into a small inductor which will not radiate, thus
preserving the low angle radiation of the antenna.

Shown in Fig. 7 is a design for the high
frequency bands. The transmission line is decoupled
from the field of the antenna by coiling it into an
rf choke at the antenna base.

Antenna matching is accomplished by tapping the
transmission line on the base coil which should be
inclosed in a waterproof container. Coil inductance

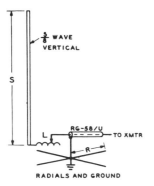

BAND	LENGTH S		LENGTH R	
	FEET	METERS	FEET	METERS
80	153'9"	46.9	62'0"	18.9
40	81'11"	25.0	33'0"	10.1
30	57'9	17.6	23'0"	7.0
20	41'3"	12.6	16'6"	5.0
17	32'3"	9.9	13'0"	4.0
15	27'6"	8.4	11'0"	3.4
12	23'5"	7.2	9'4"	2.9
10	19'9"	6.0	8'3"	2.5

FOR 20-6 METERS L = 10 TURNS #12 SPACEWOUND
2" (5 CM) DIAM.
FOR 80-40 METERS L = 40 TURNS AS ABOVE

Fig. 7 HF 5/8-wave DX antenna provides 3 dB gain over a ground plane. Antenna is resonated by adjusting inductor at base. At least three radials should be used with this antenna.

and antenna height are interlocking and different dimensions in one can be made up by altering the other.

Building the Antenna

The vertical portion of the extended ground plane is made of sections of telescoping tubing. A chart of tubing diameters is given later in this handbook. At least one set of insulated guy wires is required for the smaller antennas and two sets are required for the larger ones.

The radials for the antenna can be made either of aluminum tubing or wire. If the antenna is mounted above ground level, the radials can possibly serve as guy wires to steady the assembly. Many amateurs have had excellent results with the antenna mounted on the roof of their residence, with the radials running along the surface of the roof. Others have post-mounted the antenna with the radials fanning out at 6 to 8 feet (1.8 to 2.5 m) above ground. The loading coil is mounted in a waterproof box at the

base of the antenna with the feedline brought into
the box via a waterproof joint.

Tuning the Antenna

After the antenna is assembled and mounted in
place, the vertical section is shorted to the
radials via a two-turn coil which is coupled to a
dip meter. Loading coil inductance or antenna length
is adjusted so as to provide a resonance indication
at the design frequency.

The next step is to match the antenna to the
transmission line. This is accomplished by moving
the tap, a quarter-turn at a time, up from the
bottom of the coil and noting the SWR on the
transmission line after each setting. Once an SWR
null has been found near the design frequency, an
SWR sweep across the band is advised, and the SWR
plotted against frequency on a graph. This curve
should be saved for future reference. Slight
adjustments to tap and coil can "zero-in" the SWR to
unity at the design frequency.

Short, Loaded Radials

What to do when ground plane radials are longer
than the space available? A solution to this problem
is to insert a loading coil in each radial to
establish resonance. Radials as short as 0.1
wavelength have been loaded to 0.25 wavelength in
this manner.

The loading coil should be placed in the middle
of the radial. Typical radial length and coil
inductance are given in Fig. 8. As in the case of a
coil-loaded antenna, the radials should be resonant
at the design frequency. This can be accomplished by
connecting two radials together via a two-turn coil
to form a dipole element. The coil is coupled to a
dip meter and the radial tips are trimmed equally
until resonance is established.

Band	Radial Length Ft. (Meters)	Loading Coil (μH)
160	63.3 (19.29)	91.6
80	33.5 (10.21)	40.8
40	16.3 (4.96)	19.9
30	11.5 (3.5)	13.4
20	8.3 (2.53)	9.0
17	6.5 (1.98)	6.8
15	5.5 (1.67)	5.7
12	4.6 (1.40)	4.7
10	4.0 (1.22)	4.0
6	2.3 (0.7)	2.0

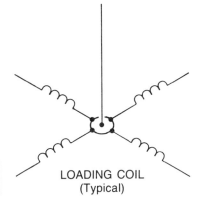

LOADING COIL
(Typical)

Fig. 8 Short, coil-loaded radials for ground plane antenna. Radials should be resonated at desired frequency as operating bandwidth is less than that of conventional radials.

Coil-loaded radials are quite frequency sensitive and limit the operating bandwidth of the antenna more than conventional radials do. Even so, if the space permits nothing else, this is the way to do the job.

The Inverted Ground Plane

Raising the ground plane in the air helps in two ways. First, it elevates the radiating element from the lossy ground and second, it gets the area of maximum current up in the air where it can do some good. If you cannot get your ground plane up in the air, the next best thing to do is invert it!

The inverted ground plane was first tried in the early "forties" and was gaining popularity when radio amateur activity was closed down during World War II. After the war it was forgotten until it was made the basis of a "hot" beam antenna, to be described in the next chapter.

The basic inverted ground plane is shown in Fig. 9. It consists of a base-fed, quarter-wave vertical section, connected to two quarter-wave radials at

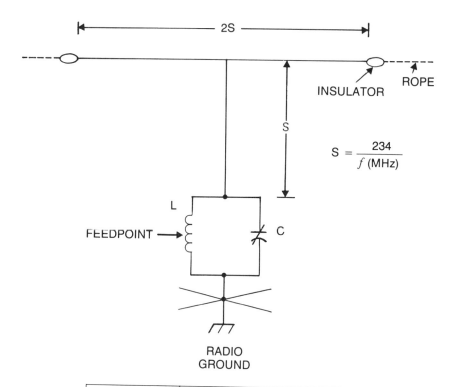

$$S = \frac{234}{f \text{ (MHz)}}$$

BAND	L (μH)	C(pF)
40	10	50
30	7	40
20	5	25
17	4	20
15	3	20
12	2	15
10	2	15

Fig. 9 Inverted ground plane provides good, low angle signal for DX contacts. Antenna provides about 2 dB more radiation in-line with flat top than at right angles to it.

the top. The radials can serve as supports for the vertical wire, making an inexpensive and easily installed antenna.

Since only two radials are used, the radiation pattern is not truly omnidirectional, providing about 2 dB more radiation in-line with the radials than at right angles to them.

The inverted ground plane is fed with a parallel tuned circuit which is adjusted to resonance with a dip meter. Next, a small amount of power is fed to the antenna and the tap on the inductor moved back and forth, a bit at a time, until the point of least SWR is found. Circuit tuning should then be touched up for minimum SWR reading.

The ground connection for the inverted ground plane carries little rf current and a single ground rod and screen (such as described for the Bobtail beam in the next chapter) will suffice.

A Helical Antenna for 40 Meters

Many amateurs require a low profile antenna and even a quarter-wave vertical antenna for the lower frequency bands can be too tall under some circumstances. Shown in this section is a 40 meter ground plane antenna that is only 16 feet (4.9 m) high. It consists of a helical-wound vertical antenna using three wire radials (Fig. 10).

The vertical element is wound on a 17 foot (5.3 m) long varnished bamboo pole, or section of plastic pipe. The pole is wound with no. 18 enamel wire. The top 11 feet (3.35 m) of the pole is wound at a pitch of one turn per 1.5 inch (3.8 cm). This is followed by a closewound coil of 26 turns of no. 14 enamel wire. Coil diameter is one inch (2.54 cm). The next portion of the winding consists of 48 inches (1.22 m) wound at a pitch of one turn per inch. The bottom winding of the helix consists of 16 turns of no. 18 spacewound the wire diameter.

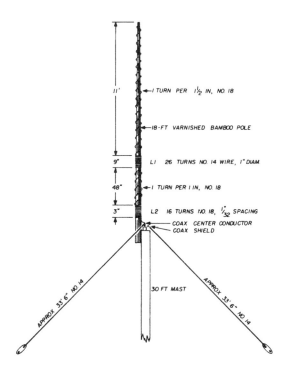

Fig. 10 Helical-wound ground plane antenna for 40 meters. Element is dipped to frequency and trimmed by means of base coil.

The antenna is adjusted to 7.25 MHz (or any other frequency in the 7 MHz band) by resonating it with a dip meter. The antenna is placed in position and connected to the radial system via a small two turn coil. The coil is coupled to the dip meter. Antenna resonance is set by adjusting the bottom coil of the helix a turn at a time.

Antenna bandwidth between the 2-to-1 SWR points on the feedline is about 100 kHz. (A version of this antenna was described by John McFarland, W4ROS, in the May, 1971 issue of "Ham Radio" magazine.)

Chapter 6

Phased Vertical Arrays

Two or more vertical antennas can be combined into an array whose field pattern is the sum of the fields of each of the antennas. The combined field is a function of the spacing between the individual antennas, the power in each, and the electrical phase difference between them. Arrays of this type are common in broadcast and low frequency service and simplified versions of these antennas are useful for amateur hf communication.

Element Phasing

Unlike the parasitic Yagi array, all elements in a phased array are fed power directly from the transmitter. Each element is in the near-field of another element and the elements react upon each other so that the feedpoint resistance of all of the elements is changed.

In broadcast arrays, the feedpoint resistances are matched because the null in the pattern of the array is carefully positioned so as to protect another broadcaster on the same channel. Amateur phased arrays have no need of such null-protection and the complex networks necessary to match the elements in a phased array are not commonly used.

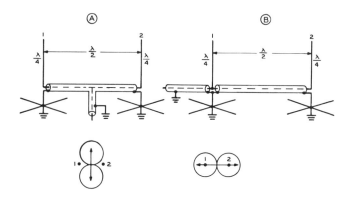

Fig. 1 Field patterns of phased vertical antennas. At left is broadside pattern of two elements fed in-phase. At right is pattern of out-of-phase antennas. Lengths shown are electrical, not physical.

The desired phase shift between the elements in an amateur band phased array can be controlled by the physical spacing of the elements and the electrical length of the coax line that connects them together. An electrical half-wave line is equivalent to a phase shift of 180 degrees; a quarter-wave is equal to a shift of 90 degrees, and so on. By changing the length of the line and the element spacing, the field pattern of the phased array can be moved about without moving the elements. Fig. 1 indicates representative field patterns that can be obtained from two vertical antennas. In general, if two antennas spaced a half-wavelength apart are fed in-phase, a figure-8 field pattern at right angles (broadside) to the plane of the two antennas is produced. If the antennas are fed 180 degrees out-of-phase, a figure-8 pattern in line with the antennas (end-fire) is generated. Finally, two antennas driven 90 degrees out-of-phase with quarter-wave spacing will produce a unidirectional, cardioid pattern in line with the antennas. The theoretical front-to-back ratio of this design is 23 dB, however coupling between the antennas unbalances the feedpoint resistances which unbalances antenna currents. The result is a drop in gain of about 0.5 dB from the maximum figure of 3 dB and a reduction of the front-to-back ratio to about 10 dB.

Power Gain of the Phased Array

As in the case of a single vertical antenna, a good ground system is required for a base-fed phased array. When the array is ground mounted, a ground screen or multiple radials, at least 0.2 wavelength long, should fan out from the base of each antenna. Some amateurs construct a large, oval-shaped radial screen that encompasses both antennas.

When two broadside half-wave antennas are fed in-phase, with half-wave separation, theoretical power gain over a single antenna is about 4 dB. In the 180 degree, out-of-phase mode power gain is approximately 2 dB. Power gain for the 90 degree, out-of-phase mode with quarter-wave spacing is 3 dB.

Three elements with half-wave spacing provide about 6 dB gain in the in-phase mode.

The Bobtail Beam

First described by W.W. Smith, W6BCX, in 1948 in the old "Radio" magazine, the Bobtail beam has proven to be a good DX antenna for the low frequency bands. It is a simplified version of a three element vertical broadside array using quarter-wave elements (Fig. 2). In the classic version, three half-wave elements are base-fed in-phase with equal currents, and the elements are spaced a half-wavelength apart. In the Bobtail beam, the center element is fed directly and the outer elements are fed via half-wave wires connecting the upper tips of all elements. Because of current reversal in the horizontal wire, there is little radiation from it.

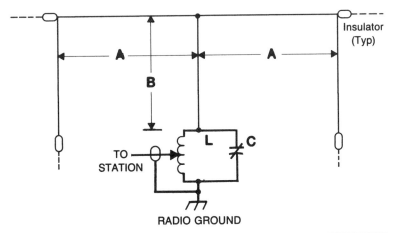

BAND	A	B	L(μH)	C(pF)
80	140.5	69.0	50	40
40	70.3	34.0	25	20
30	48.7	23.6	17	15
20	35.2	17.0	13	10

FEET X 0.3048 = METERS

Fig. 2 Base-fed, in-phase elements of Bobtail beam give pattern in and out of page. Parallel tuned resonant circuit couples antenna to coax line.

The array has a broad, figure-8 pattern at right angles (broadside) to the line of the vertical wires, and provides about 5 dB gain over a comparison ground plane antenna when the path length exceeds 2500 miles (4000 km).

The height required for an 80 meter array is about 70 feet (21.3 m), but for 40 meters, the required height is only about 30 to 40 feet (10.7 to 12.2 m).

The feedpoint resistance at the bottom of the center vertical element has a very high value at the design frequency and a parallel tuned, low-C circuit matches the antenna to a 50 or 75 ohm coax line.

Because of the high feedpoint resistance and the fact that the high current portions of the array are elevated above ground, ground current is very low and an elaborate ground system is not necessary. A six foot (1.8 m) ground rod in conjunction with a 10 foot square (3x3 m) ground screen directly below the feedpoint are ample.

Ready-made screen material available in the USA and Canada is a 3x5 foot (0.9x1.5 m) piece of galvanized hardware cloth or chicken wire found at large home improvement stores. As many pieces as will fit into the available space should be soldered together and laid atop the ground.

Remember, the bottom of the vertical sections is "hot" with rf and can cause a bad burn if high power is run and the antenna accidentally touched. One way to avoid this is to slip some small diameter, clear plastic tubing (such as a fuel line) over the ends of the wires closer than 8 feet (2.5 m) to the ground.

Building the Bobtail Beam

The top horizontal wire of the beam is made of hard-drawn or steel core copper wire to prevent stretching. It can be suspended about head height between two points and the vertical wires soldered to it. Once the assembly is complete, it is hoisted into position and the vertical wires brought down and tied to convenient points at, or near, ground level. The tuned matching circuit is placed in a waterproof box at the base of the center element.

Tuning the Antenna

As with other antenna designs, antenna resonance can be set with a dip meter. Couple the meter to the tuned circuit and adjust it to the design frequency. Power is then applied to the antenna from the transmitter and the tap point on the coil adjusted by observing the SWR on the transmission line. Circuit tuning and tap placement are somewhat interlocking and the antenna should always be brought into resonance after a tap point change is made.

The last step is to make an SWR sweep across the band and log the reverse readings at 50 or 100 kHz intervals. The design frequency of the antenna can be moved about by retuning the matching circuit.

A Half-Bobtail Array for 80,40,or 30 Meters

Not enough room for a full-size Bobtail beam? Then consider a half-size Bobtail having only two vertical elements. Referring to Fig. 2, the smaller array would consist of the driven element and one horizontal wire running to a single top-fed element. (The array is sometimes called a "half-square antenna".) The field pattern is at right angles to the plane of the array and quite broad. Power gain over a ground plane is about 3 dB when the path length exceeds 2500 mi. (4000 km).

This antenna can operate on several other bands. It serves as a quarter-wave Marconi on the next lower frequency band and can be operated against ground with a matching network. On the next higher frequency band, it acts as an end-fed wire. It can be tuned to any point in this band by resonating the tuned circuit to the higher frequency. The input tap need not be adjusted.

A Two Element Base-fed Array

This feed system overcomes the current unbalance problem common in a two element array and provides a cardioid field pattern with a forward gain of 3 dB and a front-to-back ratio of better than 15 dB. It consists of two quarter-wave verticals, spaced a quarter-wave apart and base-fed 90 degrees

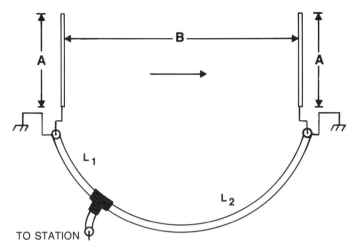

BAND	A	B	L_1	L_2
80	66.8	70.28	46.39	92.77
40	33.4	35.14	23.19	45.10
30	23.2	24.36	16.07	32.15
20	16.7	17.57	11.60	22.55

FEET X 0.3048 = METERS

Fig. 3 Two element, base-fed array provides good gain and enhanced front-to-back ratio with cardioid pattern.

out-of-phase. (Fig. 3). Eight quarter-wave radial wires are fanned out from the base of each antenna. The wires are laid on the surface of the ground.

The antennas are fed with lengths of 75 ohm coax line (RG-11/U or RG-59/U) that provide the correct phase relationship between the antennas. The phasing lines (L1, L2) are cut to length with the aid of a dip meter to ensure correct phase shift. The two lines are joined with T-connector and a single 50 or 75 ohm coax line run from this point to the station.

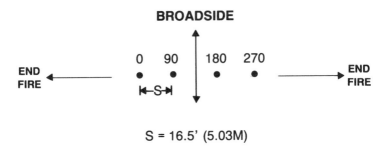

S = 16.5' (5.03M)

Fig. 4 Four elements with suitable phase shift circuit provide end-fire pattern in two directions and broadside, bi-directional pattern. Array is viewed from the top.

Each antenna is individually adjusted to the design frequency by means of a dip meter coupled to a two turn coil connected between the antenna and the ground radial system. (This antenna is patterned after the design of Roy Lewallen, W7EL, shown in the August, 1979 issue of "QST" magazine.)

A 4 Element Base-fed Array for 20 Meters

This compact and unobtrusive four element beam provides switchable directivity in line with the elements, plus a broadside lobe to provide nearly complete coverage of the compass. Directivity is switched from the operating position by means of relays. (This array is patterned after an 80 meter design of W1HKK shown in March 1965, "QST" magazine and was built by Jim Gabriel, WA8DXB, and described in "Ham Radio" magazine, May, 1983.)

Operation of the antenna is summarized in Fig. 4. In the end-fire (in-line) case, the antennas are driven with a 90 degree phase shift between them (0, 90, 180 ,and 270 degrees). This phasing provides a unidirectional pattern from the 0 degree element through the 270 degree element having a theoretical gain of about 4.9 dB over a single element. To reverse the pattern 180 degrees, the antennas are fed in the reverse order: 270, 180, 90 and 0 deg.

A third switch position provides a bidirectional broadside lobe (at right angles to the line of the array). This has a gain of about 5.3 dB.

Building the Array

The 20 meter design uses four 16.5 foot (5.03 m) elements made of 1 inch (25.4 mm), 7/8-inch (22.23 mm) and 3/4-inch (19.05 mm) tubing with .058 inch (1.45 mm) walls. These sizes telescope within each other. The outer sections of tubing are slit for a few inches and a automobile hose clamp holds the joint rigid. The elements are mounted on plastic spacers which, in turn, are mounted on 1-inch diameter treated wood dowels driven several feet into the ground.

The ground system for each vertical consists of an aluminum disc with a clearance hole cut in the center. A series of holes are drilled around the perimeter and the radials are attached to the disc by means of brass nuts and bolts.

The original installation used four quarter-wave radials (laid out on the ground) per antenna. Results were poor, so additional radials were added. Eight radials per antenna gave much improved performance. Finally, up to 30 radials per antenna were gradually added with noticeable improvement in performance.

The Feed System

The verticals are spaced 16.5 feet (5.03 m) apart and each is fed by an equal-length, 3/4-wave section of 50 ohm coax line. The same type line is used for the main feeder, the power divider and the phasing lines.

The relay box wiring is short and direct to maintain the correct phase relationship between the antennas (Fig. 5). Type-N fittings are used for the

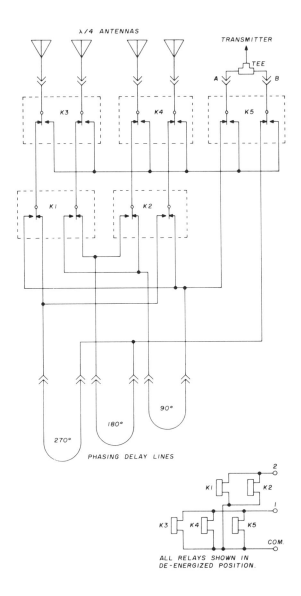

Fig. 5 Relay wiring. End-fire pattern is present with no dc applied. Dc applied to terminals 2 and COM (common) reverses array direction and applied to terminals 1 and COM provides broadside, bidirectional pattern.

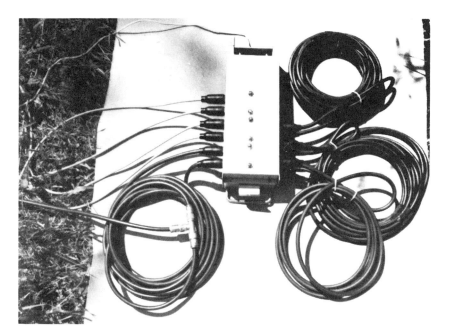

Fig. 6 Relay box showing phasing lines coiled into position. Waterproof connectors are used.

power divider and phasing line connections (Fig. 6) because they are waterproof devices. The relays are surplus 115 V, 60 Hz large-contact units that activate at about 35 Vdc.

The SWR is less than 1.4-to-1 in the end-fire modes when twelve radials per element are used. It is less than 2-to-1 in the broadside mode. Additional radials reduce the SWR in both operating modes.

A 4 Element, Square Array for 40 Meters

Described in this section is a four element, phased array designed by Jerrold Swank, W8HXR, for use at Byrd Station, Antarctica (KC4USB). The antenna was described in the May, 1975, issue of "Ham Radio" magazine.

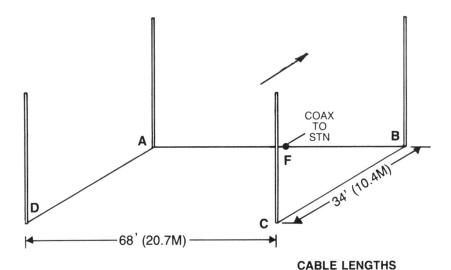

CABLE LENGTHS
A-F and F-B = 35' (10.67M)
A-D and B-C = 67'8" (20.62M)

Fig. 7 Four element, phased array used at Byrd Station, Antarctica on 40 meters. Elements are quarter-wave whips. Gain is about 6 dB over a single element. Physical spacing of elements shown in drawing.

The array combines a broadside, half-wave spaced pair of vertical elements with quarter-wave spaced elements in a square configuration. Array gain is estimated to better than 6 dB over a single vertical antenna. The radiation pattern is at right angles to the line A-B and in the direction of the arrow in Fig. 7.

The phasing lines between the quarter-wave spaced elements (A-D and B-C) are 3/4-wavelength long because when the velocity factor of the cable (0.66) is taken into consideration, a quarter-wave line is too short to span the distance. The longer line provides the same phase delay.

A T-connection is located at the center of the line connecting the half-wave spaced elements. These are connected to the T with equal-length lines, line length being noncritical in this instance.

The antennas are supported about 6 feet (1.8 m) above ground and the radials extend out to ground level. The radials are placed in front of the elements to provide the best ground plane in the desired direction.

This array has been tested against a large log-periodic antenna mounted on a 100 foot (30.4 m) tower over the Antarctic-USA path and provides an average signal within 3 decibels of that of the much-larger beam.

Adjusting Coax Line Phasing Sections

The radio wave travels more slowly in a coax line than it does in free space, so the wavelength along a line is less than the free space wavelength for a given frequency.

The result is that the physical length of a given line section is always somewhat less than the electrical length. The velocity factor of a line is the ratio of the actual wave velocity along the line compared to the velocity in free space. For conventional lines with a solid polyethylene dielectric, the factor is approximately 0.66. The coax line length corresponding to an electrical quarter-wavelength, then, for a given frequency is about (246 x 0.66)/f, where 0.66 is the velocity factor and f is the frequency in megahertz.

Because the velocity of propagation of coaxial lines varies slightly depending upon manufacturing techniques, it is important to cut the line to length with the aid of a dip meter. The length of connecting plugs, if any, should be taken into account.

Cutting the Line

As an example, assume a coax line is to be cut to a quarter-wavelength at 7.15 MHz. Approximate line length is (246 x 0.66)/f, or 147.6/7.15 = 20.42 feet (6.22 m).To be on the safe side, a section of line is cut about 21 feet (6.4 m) long. Before measurements are undertaken, a coaxial plug is placed on one end of the line. The other end is trimmed even and the outer conductor edge tinned with a soldering gun to prevent some of the braid wires from shorting to the center conductor. A single turn loop just large enough to fit snugly over the coil of a dip meter is soldered between the braid and the center conductor.

The coax line is straightened out and the dip meter loosely coupled to the coil. The frequency of the dip meter is measured on a nearby receiver. The indication of resonance on the dip meter shows the resonant frequency of the cable length. Make several readings and take an average to obtain the most accurate measurement. You should be able to have the readings agree within a few kilohertz.

Since the cable is originally cut slightly long, the indicated frequency will be lowered than that desired. Cut one inch (2.54 cm) off the cable and reconnect the loop. Repeat the measurements and determine the new resonant frequency. This will tell you how many kilohertz the cable moves in frequency when one inch is trimmed from the end. If, for example, the original set of readings indicated a resonant frequency of 7.00 MHz, and trimming one inch from the line raised the frequency 50 kHz to 7.05 MHz, then trimming an additional two inches (5 cm) from the line will raise the resonant frequency 100 kHz to 7.15 MHz.

If a second coax plug is to be placed on the line, the line will have to be trimmed back a bit as total line length is measured from plug tip to plug tip.

Chapter 7

Multiband Vertical Antennas

As discussed in an earlier chapter, any antenna can be adjusted to operate on any frequency provided the proper tuning network is used. It is important, however, to remember that most practical multiband antennas are approximately an electrical quarter wavelength long at the lowest operating frequency. This chapter shows some interesting variations on this idea.

A Simple Multiband Vertical Antenna

An inexpensive multiband antenna is a single element tuned to resonance by a loading coil. A popular version consists of a 20 foot (6.1 m) section of aluminum tubing, base loaded by an adjustable coil and operated against ground (Fig. 1). Operation on any band between 10 and 80 meters is accomplished by proper placement of the taps on the coil. The connections are made with an inductance clip, such as the Barker & Williamson 3942, or equivalent. The base coil is a section of air-wound inductor.

For temporary service the antenna can be used with a ground rod, but a more permanent and efficient installation would require a ground screen or multiple radial wires.

Operating bandwidth of this simple antenna is over 150 kHz on 20 meters and above, about 80 kHz on 40 meters and approximately 35 kHz on 80 meters.

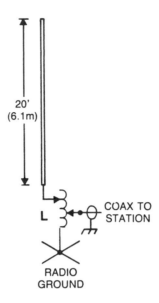

Fig. 1 Multiband vertical for 80 through 15 meter bands. Coil taps and feed-point are adjusted on each band by means of SWR meter in feedline. Coil is 35 turns, 2-1/2 inches diam., 6 turns per inch (B & W 3029 or equivalent).

The antenna is clamped to a rectangular mounting plate with U-bolts. The plate, in turn, is mounted to a ground post or other support by two ceramic standoff insulators. Alternatively, the antenna can be slipped within a telescoping section of plastic PVC pipe fastened to the support with U-bolts.

The approximate coil taps for a particular band are chosen and a few watts of power are applied to the antenna through an SWR meter. The antenna tap is shifted a bit for lowest SWR and the feedpoint tap is then adjusted to minimize the SWR reading. The adjustments are slightly interlocking. When the optimum tap points are found, they are logged and the procedure is repeated for another band.

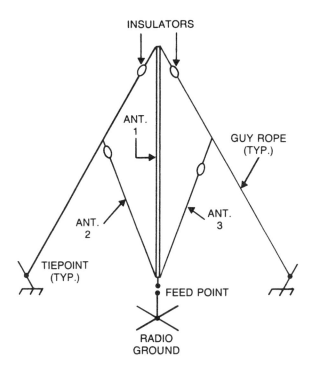

INSULATORS

ANT.
1

GUY ROPE
(TYP.)

ANT.
2

ANT.
3

TIEPOINT
(TYP.)

FEED POINT

RADIO
GROUND

Fig. 2 Vertical antenna plus sloping guy ropes support other antennas for higher frequency bands. A popular combination is 20-15-10 meters. Separation between antennas at the top is about 3 feet (0.9m).

An Inexpensive Triband Vertical Antenna

Vertical antennas for different amateur bands can be connected in parallel at the feedpoint and fed with one transmission line, as shown in Fig. 2. The antennas are fanned out slightly to achieve minimum interaction between them. Because isolation between the elements is not perfect, SWR at resonance of the antennas is not as low as it would be if separate feed systems were used. An L-network placed at the transmitter will reduce the SWR to a very low value

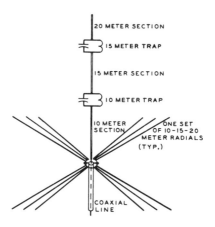

Fig. 3 Trap vertical antenna for 10, 15 and 20 meters. The traps act as electrical switches and disconnect antenna sections as the frequency of operation is changed.

and may be required if a solid-state transmitter is used.

In this design, the vertical antenna for the lowest frequency band is made of aluminum tubing and acts as a support for the ropes holding the wire verticals. The ropes also act as guy wires for the tubing section. For best antenna efficiency a ground screen or multiple ground wires are required.

The Multiband Trap Antenna

The vertical antenna is a frequency-sensitive device capable of providing a good match to the transmission line over a narrow operating range. A matching device is often used to resonate it at off-resonance frequencies, but a more practical and useful means to achieve multiband operation is to change the length of the antenna as the band in use is changed. If the antenna is cut for operation on the lowest band, sections of the antenna can be disconnected, or decoupled, for operation on higher freqency bands. A remote switch will do the job, but an easier way is to use automatic decoupling traps, as shown in Fig. 3.

A typical trap consists of a high impedance resonant circuit. The high impedance of the trap isolates an unwanted portion of the antenna, permitting the remaining section to resonate at the desired frequency.

In the illustration, the bottom trap is resonant at 10 meters, isolating the upper portion of the antenna. A second trap, adjusted to 15 meters, is placed higher in the element to isolate a somewhat shorter section of the antenna. The complete antenna element, including the two traps, resonates at 20 meters. Theoretically, an antenna could be made to resonate on any number of frequencies lower than the fundamental frequency by adding a sufficient number of additional sections and traps.

The Decoupling Trap

A popular trap design consists of coil and capacitor resonant in the highest operating band of the antenna. If the impedance of the trap is sufficiently high (10,000 ohms, or more), it is nearly equivalent to an open switch. At or near the resonant trap frequency, the element section after it is effectively disconnected from the antenna. The antenna section between the trap and the feedpoint is resonant at a frequency determined by its electrical length and diameter, plus any residual effect contributed by the presence of the trap.

At the lowest frequency of operation of the trapped antenna, the traps act somewhat in the manner of loading coils whose effect is to shorten the physical length of the antenna. A multiband,

trapped antenna therefore will have slightly shorter
dimensions than a single element for the same
frequency. The amount of shortening depends to a
large extent upon the design and construction of the
trap.

A practical multiband antenna is a series of
engineering and electrical compromises as the
factors contributing to a highly efficient, low-loss
trap are at odds with the need for a compact,
waterproof, low price unit capable of working in an
outdoor environment. It is a tribute to antenna
engineers that many of the popular triband antennas
on the market work as well as they do. In any event,
the small loss in efficiency in a well designed trap
does not seem too great a penalty to pay for the
convenience of multiband operation with a single
antenna.

Radials for the Multiband Antenna

A multiband vertical requires a good ground
system for each band in order to do its job. If the
antenna is ground mounted, multiple ground radials
or a ground screen should be used. The radials
and/or screen should be large enough for efficient
operation on the lowest frequency band in use.

If the antenna is elevated above ground, multiple
radials should be placed beneath it. It is common
practice to make the number of radials on the higher
bands equal to the total number of radials for the
lowest band. For example, a 20-15-10 meter antenna
may have 4 radials for 20 meters, and two radials
each for 15 and 10 meters. Many amateurs, of course,
use more radials than this.

A Vertical Antenna for 3.5, 7, 10 and 14 MHz

A 5/8-wave vertical antenna for 14 MHz provides
about 3 dB gain over the conventional quarter-wave
antenna. That is equivalent to doubling the

transmitter power. In addition, the extra antenna height allows operation on the lower frequency bands if a suitable matching network is used.

A practical design is shown in Fig. 4. Eight radials, 60 feet (18.3 m) long, are fanned out on the surface of the ground and an 8 foot (2.44 m) long ground rod is driven into the earth at the base of the antenna.

Antenna feedpoint impedance is reactive on all bands and shows a resistance value of about 20 ohms on 80 meters, 180 ohms on 40 meters, 900 ohms on 30 meters and 40 ohms on 20 meters. A pi-network that will match this range of values is shown in the drawing. The network is placed at the base of the antenna in a waterproof wood box.

Building the Antenna

The antenna is 41 feet (12.5 m) high and built of sections of aluminum tubing. The bottom section is a 20 foot (6.1 m) length of 2 inch (5.1 cm) diameter irrigation pipe. The top three sections are made of telescoping sections of tubing, all having a wall thickness of .058 inch (1.47 mm). Diameters of the sections are 1.75 inches (4.45 cm), 1.5 inches (3.81 cm) and 1.375 inches (3.49 cm). The antenna is supported by a 4x4 (10 cm square) wood post 8 feet (2.44 m) long. The bottom half of the post is painted and then wrapped with two layers of heavy weight aluminum kitchen foil which covers the sides and end. The foil is held in place with vinyl tape, and seams in the foil are also taped. This protects the post against ground water rot and termites. The post is sunk about 4 feet (1.22 m) in the ground.

The antenna is mounted to the post by three heavy duty ceramic standoff insulators. The better insulators have metal bases which add strength to the mounting area. The whole assembly is very rugged and requires no guying. The top of the antenna will

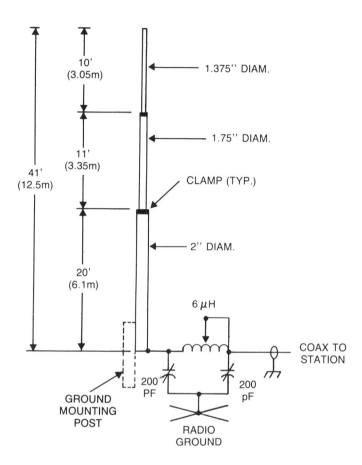

Fig. 4 Gain antenna for 80-10 meters. This design provides about 3 dB gain on 20 meters and less on the lower frequency bands. A simple pi-network at base permits the antenna to be tuned to the band in use. Tuning data is given in text. A smaller version, 22 feet (6.7 m) high can be used on the 20-15-10 meter bands. Network component values are reduced by half for the higher frequency design.

sway about 2 feet   (0.6 m) in a heavy   wind   with   no
harm done to it.

Tuning the Antenna

The pi-network   consists of two capacitors   and a
tapped   coil. The   antenna capacitor (at the left   in
the   drawing) is   only used   on   the 30 and 40   meter
bands. On   the other bands   it   is set   at   zero. The
right-hand capacitor and the coil   are   adjusted   for
lowest value of SWR on   the feedline.   On 30   and   40
meters   the left capacitor   brings   the network   into
resonance   and the right capacitor   will   be set near
zero value.

Using the Antenna on 14 Thru 30 MHz

The antenna design shown   in the previous section
can be adapted for use   on the higher frequency bands
by cutting the overall   length to   22   feet (6.7 m).
The   basic antenna is now a half-wave vertical for 21
MHz, which also functions as   a 5/8-wave vertical   on
28 MHz,   providing   about   3   dB   gain on the   latter
band.   On   the   24   MHz   band,   about 2   dB   gain   is
provided. The network capacitors   are reduced to   100
pF   and the coil   inductance to   3 uH   for   the   high
frequency version of   the antenna. The ground   system
consists of   eight radial   wires,   30   feet   (9.1   m)
long, plus an 8 foot (2.44 m) ground rod at   the base
of the antenna.

A Vertical for 40 and 75 Meters

This compact antenna employs   a   single trap   and
top-hat loading   and   is only   33   feet (10   m)   high
(Fig.   5).   It is   designed for rooftop   mounting and
has four radials-- two for   40 meters   and two for 80
meters.   The   latter   are   bent   into   a   Z-shape   to

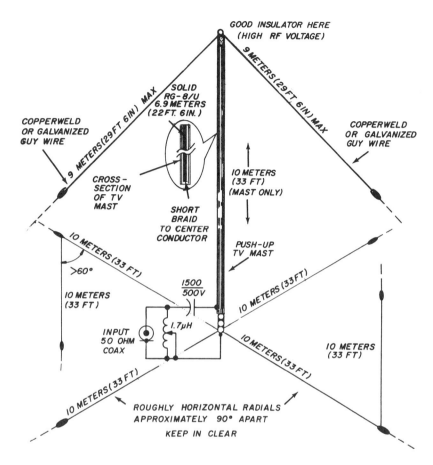

Fig. 5 A two-band vertical antenna for 40 and 80 meters. The vertical mast is resonant on 40 meters. Top loading resonates it in the 80 meter band. The decoupling trap, made of a shorted section of coax cable, is dropped down inside the mast. A simple L-network at the antenna base provides a match to a 50 or 75 ohm coax line. The shunt inductor is adjusted for lowest SWR at the 80 meter design frequency. Antenna is mounted to a wood post by means of U-bolts.

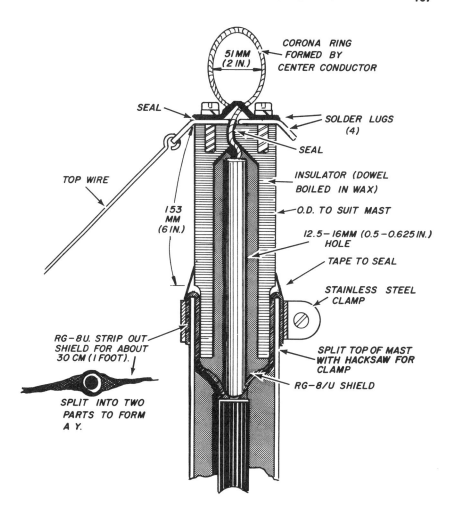

Fig. 6 View of the top assembly of the two-band vertical antenna. Outer braid of the coax decoupling trap is split into two pig-tails which are clamped to the top of the mast. The inner conductor of the coax passes up through the top insulator and is attached to the two top wire guys which act as loading wires. 80 meter resonant frequency can be changed by adjusting wire length.

conserve roof space. A simple L-network provides a good impedance match on both bands. Operational bandwidth between the 2-to-1 SWR points on the feedline is about 120 kHz on 80 meters and 220 kHz on 40 meters.

Building the Antennna

The antenna is made from a three section push-up TV mast which is trimmed to one quarter wavelength on 40 meters. From the top a length of RG-8A/U (RG-213/U) is dropped down inside the mast. The line is 22.5 feet (6.9 m) long with the shield shorted to the inner conductor at the bottom end. This joint is wrapped with vinyl tape to prevent it from shorting to the mast. The top outer shield is connected to the top of the TV mast. The top center conductor of the coax is connected to two slanted top-hat wires, which act as guy wires and a capacitive loading element. On 40 meters the coax appears as a parallel resonant circuit and isolates the mast from the top hat radial wires. On 75 meters the coax is one eighth wavelength long and acts as a series loading coil. The mast, coaxial coil and top hat form a series resonant circuit, forming a one eighth wave radiator resonant at about 3850 kHz.

The Matching Network

On 40 meters the feedpoint resistance is about 40 ohms. On 75 meters, because of top loading, the base resistance is about 18 ohms. (If base loading were used, the feedpoint resistance would only be about 7 ohms.) The network is adjusted for proper 75 meter operation and is left in the circuit for 40 meter operation as it has negligible effect on this band.

Antenna Details

The detail of the top of the mast is shown in Fig. 6. This is a high voltage point so a good quality top insulator is needed. The one used was cut from a hard maple block and painted with G.C. "Insu-volt" varnish. Micarta, Teflon, Lexan, or other insulating materials are suitable. The top end of the coax cable within the mast is sealed with a coat of G.E. RTV-108 sealant, or equivalent.

The two top radials are made of galvanized iron or copperweld wire. They have low current in them and wire size is not important, but they must withstand wind stress. The lower end of the radials terminates in a strain insulator.

A corona ring is formed at the top of the mast by extending the center conductor of the coax to form a 2 inch (51 mm) diameter loop. This is necessary if high power is run in damp weather.

The base insulator is at a low voltage point and is made of a painted hard wood block. To stabilize the antenna a second set of guy wires is placed at the top of the base section of the mast. Guy rings are usually supplied with the mast.

The L-network is placed in a waterproof wood box at the base of the antenna. The resonant radials are run across the roof and mounted a few inches above it. The ends are supported and terminated by small insulators. The radials are bent to fit the shape of the roof, if necessary.

(This antenna was designed and built by Paul Scholz, W6PYK, and was described in the September, 1979 issue of "Ham Radio" magazine.)

A Three Band Ground Plane Antenna

This low-cost, high performance antenna is designed for 20, 15 and 10 meter operatioon and is about 9 feet (2.74 m) high (Fig. 7). The vertical

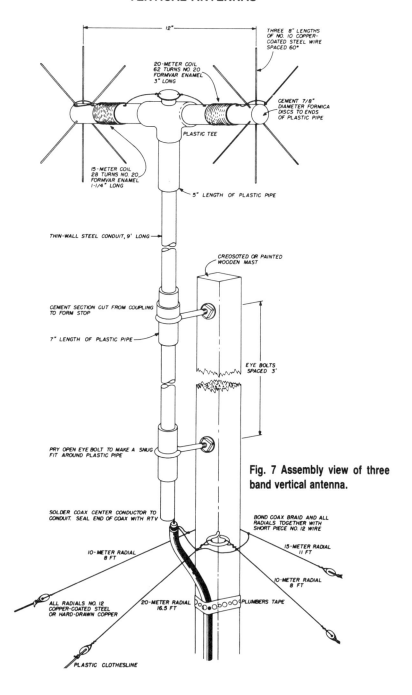

Fig. 7 Assembly view of three band vertical antenna.

portion is made of thin-wall electrical conduit, available in 10 foot (3.1 m) lengths from large building supply stores. Antenna length is slightly longer than derived by formula as the top loading affects 10 meter resonance.

Separate loading coils are used for 20 and 15 meters and are terminated in small capacity hats. This allows loading coils with fewer turns and helps reduce coil losses.

Antenna Construction

The conduit is capped with a 5 inch (12.7 cm) length of half-inch plastic water pipe which is actually 7/8-inch (22.22 mm) outside diameter. This provides a slip fit over the conduit. The pipe is cemented to a plastic T-fitting. The top of the T-fitting is drilled out so that the conduit passes through for connections to the loading coils.

A 14-inch (35.6 cm) length of plastic pipe passes horizontally through the T-fitting and the loading coils are wound on the ends of the pipe after it is cemented to the fitting. The coils are close-wound with no. 20 enamel wire. Twenty eight turns are required for the 15 meter coil and 62 turns for the 20 meter coil. The inductance of the coils can be reduced, if necessary, by removing turns. It is best to start with a few too many turns and remove a half-turn at a time until the frequency of minimum SWR is near the band center. The inductors can be fine-tuned by changing the spacing between the turns. Fortunately, there is little interaction between 15 and 20 meter resonance.

When the coils are completed, they are given a coat of G.C. "Insu-volt" varnish or acrylic spray to protect them from the weather. The resonant frequency will be lowered about 150 kHz when the coils are sprayed, so it is a good idea to have resonance about that much higher in frequency before painting starts. The conduit is zinc-plated but should be sprayed with clear lacquer as further rust preventative.

The loading coils for 20 and 15 meters are terminated by capacity hats made from three pieces of no. 10 copper wire forced through holes drilled in the end of the plastic caps.

This antenna has worked well with only four radials--two for 10 meters, one for 15 meters and one for 20 meters. These serve as guy wires, forming a drooping ground plane. If more radials can be installed, a minimum of four per band is suggested.

Antenna bandwidth between the 2-to-1 SWR points on the feedline is over 1700 kHz on 10 meters, with the design frequency at 29 MHz. This allows excellent operation over the whole band. The SWR bandwidth on 15 meters is over 600 kHz and is better than 300 kHz on 20 meters when the antenna is adjusted for resonance at 14.2 MHz. (This design was described by Fred Brown, W6HPH, in the October, 1968 issue of "Ham Radio" magazine.

Chapter 8

Antenna Roundup

The G3HCT Minibeam for 40 Meters

This simple beam antenna for 40 meters is low in cost and occupies a minimum of space. It consists of a two-wire vertical antenna supported by a 36 foot (11 m) high wood mast plus a three wire reflector. A simple coax matching system is used to match a 50 or 75 ohm line (Fig. 1).

The folded unipole element is 34 feet (10.36 m) high, with 3-1/2 inch (9 cm) spacing between the wires. The spacers are cut from short lengths of 1/2 inch (1.3 cm) diameter plastic rod, drilled to pass the wires.

Each reflector wire is 71 feet (21.64 m) long. They are supported at one point atop the tower but there is no connection between the wires. The wires clear the ground at the lower end by about 4 feet (1.22 m).

A stub matching system is used. Length D is from the antenna feedpoint to a coax T-connector. Length E is set for lowest SWR at the midpoint of the band by shorting through the coax line with a pin. When the correct spot is determined, the line is cut and the end shorted with a permanent joint.

At least eight quarter-wave radial wires are laid out on the ground surface, fanning out from the base of the antenna.

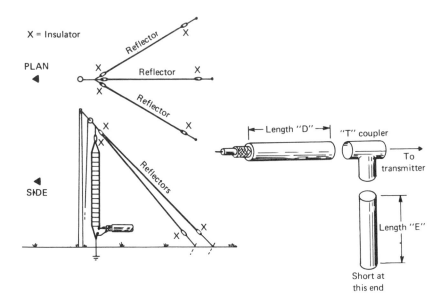

Fig. 1 The G3HCT reflector-antenna for 40 meters. A coax transformer matches antenna to 50 or 75 ohm line. Dimension D is 16'2'' (4.93 m). Dimension E is 9'3'' (2.82 m). Length E is adjusted for lowest SWR on the transmission line as explained in the text.

G3HCT reports good front-to-back ratio. Gain measurements were not made, but the antenna compares favorably with a two element Yagi on a 120 foot (36 m) high tower, usually running about 1/2 to 1 S-unit below the larger beam. G3HCT says this is "the best 40 meter antenna I've ever used".

(This antenna was originally described in "Radio Communication", a publication of the Radio Society of Great Britain and discussed in the October, 1979 issue of "CQ" magazine by Bill Orr, W6SAI.)

A Vertically Polarized Delta Loop Antenna

The vertically polarized delta loop antenna (Fig. 2) is a popular DX performer for the 30, 40 and 80 meter bands. In its simplest version, it is a one-wavelength wire, wrapped into a triangle with

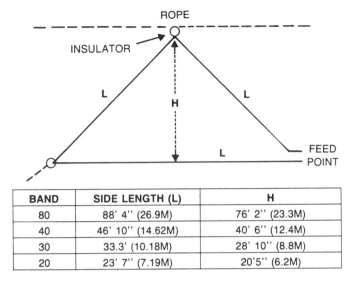

BAND	SIDE LENGTH (L)	H
80	88' 4" (26.9M)	76' 2" (23.3M)
40	46' 10" (14.62M)	40' 6" (12.4M)
30	33.3' (10.18M)	28' 10" (8.8M)
20	23' 7" (7.19M)	20'5" (6.2M)

Fig. 2 Delta loop provides 1.5 dB gain over vertical dipole. Loop is fed through quarter-wave coax transformer.

the apex at the top and fed in one corner. Depending upon the shape of the loop and the height of the bottom wire above ground, the feedpoint resistance runs between 80 and 120 ohms, providing a convenient match for a 50 or 75 ohm coax line, either direct or through a 75 ohm impedance matching line section. The line is coiled into a six turn rf choke at the point it is connected to the loop to decouple the outer shield from unwanted antenna currents.

The delta loop provides about 1.5 dB gain over a vertical dipole, and has a bidirectional radiation pattern at right angles to the plane of the loop. The high efficiency of the antenna indicates that the physical arrangement of the wire is relatively unimportant, however the loop gain and feedpoint resistance are highest when the wire encompasses the greatest area. Operational bandwidth is excellent; an 80 meter loop covers the whole band with an SWR of less than 1.8-to-1.

Feeding the Delta Loop for Multiband Operation

If the 80 meter delta loop is fed with a balanced, two-wire line and an antenna tuner or Transmatch, it can be operated on its harmonic frequencies. As the harmonic frequency increases, loop bandwidth grows and the resonant points are very broad.

For proper operation, the loop requires a top support about 45 feet (13.7 m) above ground. No radials are required if the soil below the antenna has fair to good conductivity.

The Half-sloper Antenna

A relative of the vertical antenna is the half-sloper, so-called because it is one-half of an inclined dipole. It is commonly slung from an existing metal tower, with the far end of the wire tied off near ground level (Fig. 3). The high current portion is at the top, which is beneficial for the low angle radiation which is predominantly vertically polarized. The tower is an electrical part of the antenna and plays a significant role in its operation. It must be well grounded at the base.

The half-sloper wire is fed at the top end and the shield of the coax line is attached to the tower at this point. The top of the antenna should be about a quarter-wavelength in the air and the bottom end must be well-clear of the ground (6 feet-1.8 m, or more) for best results. The included angle between wire and tower is about 45 degrees, although changes in angle and wire height may be compensated for by varying the length of the wire.

Extended tests have shown that the half-sloper provides no gain over a ground plane, but has 3 to 4 dB directivity in the direction of the slope. Apparent DX signal gain comes from the low angle of radiation provided by this unusual antenna. In

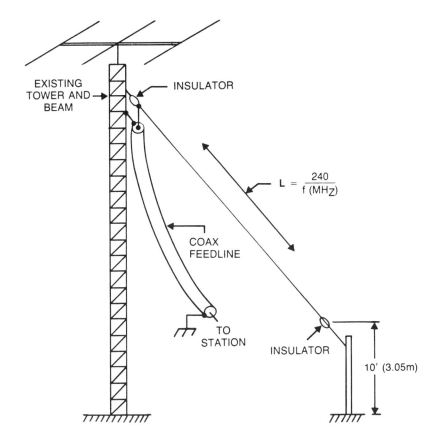

Fig. 3 The basic sloper antenna is a quarter-wave wire fed at the top and slung from an existing tower. Shield of coax is grounded to tower at the top. Lower end of sloper should clear the ground by ten feet or so.

addition, the half-sloper seems to pick up less man-made noise than the conventional vertical antenna, providing a great advantage in weak-signal reception.

Preparing the Tower for the Half-sloper Antenna

In most instances, the half-sloper is attached to an existing tower. For proper sloper operation, the

tower must act as a portion of the antenna system.
It should have good electrical conductivity from top
to bottom. In the case of a crank-up or tilt-over
tower, a flexible jumper must be placed across the
mechanical joints. If a beam is atop the tower, good
tower-to-rotary mast conductivity is very important
because if it is intermittent, the SWR on the sloper
wire will fluctuate in a breeze. A flexible jumper
from tower to mast solves this problem.

The coax lines to the sloper and to the tower
antenna, plus any control cables to the rotator on
the tower, should be taped to one tower leg and
brought down to ground level. They then should be
routed to the station along the ground. If
convenient, the lines may be buried inside a garden
hose to get them out of the way. Burying cables
without good protection from ground water is a bad
practice, hence the use of the hose.

Installing the Half-sloper Antenna

The attachment point of the half-sloper should
be one-quarter wavelength, or more, above ground. If
it is greater or less than this figure, adjustments
will probably have to be made to the length of the
sloper wire and the included angle to the tower.
Varying the angle of the wire to the tower has a
marked effect upon the feedpoint resistance and
consequent SWR, whereas adjustment of sloper length
changes the resonant frequency of the antenna. The
physical length of the wire is slightly greater than
that of an equivalent quarter-wave wire. The length
can be changed to position the resonant frequency of
the half-sloper at the desired point in the amateur
band.

Guy wires and other attachments to the tower
exert influence on the sloper wire. All guys should
be broken up by strain insulators at short intervals
to prevent unwanted resonant effects and, as in the
case of the ground plane antenna, the sloper tower

must have a good radial ground system at the base.

The half-sloper antenna provides satisfactory operating bandwidth, typically 50 kHz on 160 meters, 100 kHz on 80 meters and about 200 kHz on 40 meters between the 2-to-1 SWR points on the feedline.

Building the Vertical Antenna

A rugged and permanent vertical antenna can be built from telescoping sections of aluminum tubing. When properly assembled and guyed, this antenna will withstand heavy wind and icing. Shown in Table 1 are standard sizes of aluminum tubing that telescope within one another. The commercial alloy 6061-T6 combines good mechanical strength with corrosion resistance and is available from metal supply houses in large cities. Softer alloys used for gas lines and architectural work should be avoided as their strength is low and the material bends easily.

The first assembly step is to slot one end of the larger diameter tubes with a hacksaw. The slot goes through both walls, on a line with the center axis of the tube. This permits the diameter of the tube to shrink a bit when a clamp is placed over the end. All burrs should be carefully removed from the walls of the tube and the mating sections of tubing sanded and cleaned to lessen the possibility of seizure after they are telescoped. The slot should be wide enough so that when pressure is put upon the end of the tube, the next section of tubing is held firmly in place.

Before the sections are joined, precautions must be taken to prevent corrosion at the joints. Only a minute amount of corrosion between the tubes will prevent disassembly of the antenna at a later date. An antioxidizing, conductive compound such as General Electric G-635 dielectric sealant grease, "Penetrox" or "Cual-Aid" should be smeared lightly over the mating sections of tubing. These compounds

TABLE 1 – ALUMINUM TUBING – STANDARD SIZES

Recommended for antenna construction

Outer Diam. inch	decimal	Wall inch	Inner Diam inch	lb/ft
3	(3.000)	0.125	2.700	1.33
2-1/2	(2.500)	0.125	2.250	1.10
2-1/2	(2.500)	0.083	2.334	0.74
2-1/2	(2.500)	0.083	2.084	0.66
2-1/2	(2.500)	0.065	2.120	0.52
2	(2.000)	0.083	1.834	0.59
2	(2.000)	0.065	1.870	0.45
1-7/8	(1.875)	0.058 *	1.759	0.39
1-3/4	(1.750)	0.083	1.584	0.51
1-3/4	(1.750)	0.058 *	1.634	0.36
1-5/8	(1.625)	0.058 *	1.509	0.34
1-5/8	(1.625)	0.035	1.555	0.21
1-1/2	(1.500)	0.083	1.334	0.43
1-1/2	(1.500)	0.065	1.370	0.34
1-1/2	(1.500)	0.058 *	1.384	0.31
1-1/2	(1.500)	0.049	1.402	0.26
1-1/2	(1.500)	0.035	1.430	0.18
1-3/8	(1.375)	0.058 *	1.259	0.28
1-3/8	(1.375)	0.035	1.305	0.17
1-1/4	(1.250)	0.058 *	1.134	0.26
1-1/4	(1.250)	0.049	1.152	0.21
1-1/8	(1.125)	0.058 *	1.009	0.23
1-1/8	(1.125)	0.035	1.055	0.14
1	(1.000)	0.058 *	0.884	0.20
1	(1.000)	0.049	0.902	0.17
1	(1.000)	0.035	0.930	0.12
7/8	(0.875)	0.058 *	0.759	0.18
7/8	(0.875)	0.049	0.777	0.15
3/4	(0.750)	0.058 *	0.634	0.15
3/4	(0.750)	0.049	0.652	0.13
5/8	(0.625)	0.058 *	0.509	0.12
5/8	(0.625)	0.049	0.527	0.11
1/2	(0.500)	0.058 *	0.384	0.10
1/2	(0.500)	0.035	0.430	0.06
7/16	(0.438)	0.035	0.367	0.05
3/8	(0.375)	0.058 *	0.259	0.07
5/16	(0.313)	0.058 *	0.196	0.06
1/4	(0.250)	0.058 *	0.134	0.04

* telescopes into next larger size having 0.058 wall.

form an air-tight seal as well as being good electrical conductors.

The sections are now telescoped and the joint held securely by a compression-type hose clamp. If the sections do not make a tight fit, the joint can be shimmed with thin strips of aluminum. In any event, there should be no movement in the joint when the completed antenna is picked up at one end.

Antenna Hardware

Care must be taken to use hardware that will not rust or corrode. Never use stove bolts or any bolts that lack a corrosion-proof finish. Most industrial hardware is made of cadmium- or zinc-plated metal. This is satisfactory, provided the antenna owner checks it every year as exposure to the weather gradually deteriorates the protective plating and the hardware rusts. The best and most expensive hardware to use is stainless steel, but this is difficult to find.

All plated hardware should be given a protective coat of General Electric RTV-108 adhesive sealant or Zinc Chromate paint. The paint can be found at large hardware and home improvement stores in an Aerosol dispenser. Do not breathe the paint fumes as they are toxic.

If possible, use hexagonal-headed bolts and elastic stop nuts for antenna assembly. If stop nuts are not used, lock washers are mandatory. The use of slot-head bolts is not recommended as it is easy for the screwdriver to slip out of the bolt head, possibly inflicting a bad wound on the assembler.

By following these suggestions, the builder can make an antenna that is safe and easy to erect and simple to take apart.

Antenna Guys

Large antennas require guy wires to prevent them from whipping about in the wind. A broken guy is a safety hazard and the installation of guys should be done as carefully as assembly of the antenna. For most light amateur vertical antennas galvanized steel guy wire, broken up by strain insulators, can be used. The guys are broken into 10 foot (3 m) lengths to prevent them from becoming a resonant part of the antenna system. Galvanized coating rusts in a few years so an annual check of guys and hardware for rust is a good idea. For large antennas or towers, stranded steel guy wire is required. Small antennas can be guyed with polypropylene rope, eliminating the need for strain insulators. Keep an eye on the rope as it stretches with age.

The Base Insulator

In most cases, the voltage at the base of a vertical antenna is high enough to cause trouble. As an example, a quarter-wave vertical with a feedpoint resistance of 35 ohms has a base-to-ground voltage of about 185 volts with 1000 watts applied to the antenna. This is enough to give the unwary a bad burn so the base of the antenna should be protected against the curious.

Any good insulating material can be used for the base insulator. Hard, maple wood is a good choice if it is provided with a protective coat of General Cement Co. "Insul-volt" varnish (G.C. 10-608) or several coats of varnish or shellac. A surplus ceramic insulator will do the job for a small antenna. Some amateurs use an empty soft drink glass bottle as an antenna base insulator! Others mount their vertical directly to a ground post with U-bolts. All of these ideas, and others you may think up, will work.

Lightning Protection

If an antenna receives a direct lightning strike it may be badly damaged or vaporized. A lightning bolt can discharge over 20,000 amperes in a few seconds. Antenna, feedline and radio equipment can be destroyed with possible fatal burn or shock to the operator, if he is in the vicinity.

For this reason it is important that the feedline from antenna to station be disconnected. The feedline should be grounded outside the station to bleed off static electricity that may build up on the antenna.

A degree of equipment protection can be achieved from nearby lightning strikes (which can induce abnormally high transient voltages in the antenna) by the inclusion of a transient surge protector in the coax line. One such device is the Transi-trap protector (Alpha Delta Communications, Inc., Box 571, Centerville, OH 45459). This unit is placed in the coax line from antenna to the station.

Communication equipment can be protected from damage caused by induced power line surges from a nearby lightning stroke with the aid of a transient protective device such as a metal-oxide varistor (MOV) whose resistance varies with the magnitude of the voltage surge. The device is placed on the power line to the equipment. Additional information on these products may be found in a February, 1982, QST article by Collick and Stuart.

The National Fire Protection Association (Batterymarch Park, Quincy, MA 02269) publishes a booklet (no. 79-1983) called "Lightning Protection Code" that includes information pertinent to electronic equipment. Write for it.

Antenna Test Equipment

In order to make sure your antenna works the way it is intended to, you will need several items of inexpensive test equipment to evaluate it. The questions you will want to answer are: Is my antenna resonant at the design frequency? Does my antenna match my transmission line? Inexpensive items of test equipment will give you easy and rapid answers to these questions.

The test equipment required are an accurate SWR bridge and a dip meter. The SWR meter is often incorporated in the transmitter, but you'll have to buy or build the dip meter.

The SWR Meter

The SWR meter measures the standing wave ratio (SWR) on the transmission line to the antenna. (This is also called the "voltage standing wave ratio", or "VSWR".) The reverse reading of the meter indicates the degree of match between antenna and line. If the match is perfect (zero reverse reading on the meter), the SWR is unity, or "1-to-1". As the mismatch between antenna and line becomes greater, the reverse SWR reading rises accordingly. Most modern equipment is designed to work into a SWR as high as 2-to-1.

You can build an SWR meter if you want to, but there are good, accurate ones on the market. The inexpensive SWR meters are satisfactory for most purposes, but their reverse readings can be wildly innacurate, and often are. However, the aim is to achieve a low value of SWR on the feedline and the exact value of SWR is relatively unimportant. Buy the best SWR meter you can afford and you'll get the most accurate results. Some of the better models have plug-in rf heads for different frequency bands and will work accurately up into the vhf region.

The Dip Meter

The dip meter is a low power tunable oscillator that covers the various hf ham bands by means of plug-in coils. It has a meter that provides indication of resonance when the instrument is coupled to an antenna or other tuned circuit. The exact resonant frequency found by the dip meter can be verified by listing to the device on a nearby receiver whose dial calibration can be read to 10 kHz, or better. Commercial dip meters are available, but less expensive devices may be built up from kits.

An 80 Meter Half-sloper Cage Antenna

A conventional half-sloper antenna has a relatively narrow bandwidth and will not cover the whole 80 meter band with a reasonable value of SWR on the feedline. Shown in Fig. 4 is a multiwire sloper which provides improved bandwidth. The measured SWR is below 1.5-to-1 between 3.5 and 4.0 MHz.

The antenna consists of a 4-wire cage, 25 inches (63.5 cm) on a side and 63.5 feet (19.35 m) long. It is fed at the top, in the manner of a conventional sloper. Five spreader assemblies, made out of fiberglass rods, hold the wires in position. The spreaders are lashed together at the center points with a wrapping of stranded wire.

The end spreaders are placed so that the distance from the spreaders to the end insulators is 2 feet (0.6 m). A short nylon line is run from the crossover points of the end spreaders to the outer insulator to prevent bowing.

The cage wires are interconnected at each spreader by wire jumpers running along the

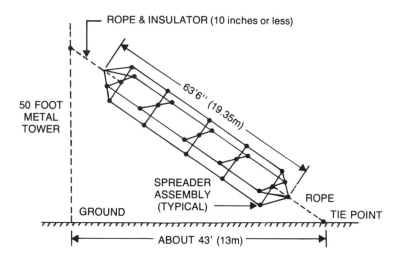

Fig. 4 Broadband sloper antenna for 80 meters. Spreaders are made of 36 inch (92cm) fiberglass rods. All wires are connected by jumpers at each spreader. SWR is less than 1.4-to-1 over 3.5 to 4.0 MHz.

spreaders. The wires are soldered together at the crosspoints.

The antenna is fastened at the 50 foot (15.3 m) level on a metal tower which may be used to support another antenna. The coax feedline is run up the tower and the shield grounded to the tower at the top. The connection wire between feedline and antenna should be not longer than 10 inches (25 cm). The coax is brought down one tower leg, along with any coax or control wires to the beam atop the tower. The lower end of the cage is about 20 feet (6.1 m) above ground level.

In general, changing the cage length changes the resonant frequency and changing the slope angle or height of the end point above ground changes the feedpoint resistance.

(This antenna is adapted from a design by Dick Jansson, WD4FAB, which was described in the August, 1983, issue of "Ham Radio" magazine.)

The HF Mobile Antenna

The success or failure of hf mobile operation depends upon the efficiency of the antenna. The mobile station runs relatively low power and must compete with high power fixed stations with good antennas. A popular mobile antenna is an 8.6 foot (2.63 m) stainless steel whip mounted on the rear of a vehicle. For 10 and 15 meter operation, antenna efficiency is high as the antenna is very near quarter-wave resonance. Feedpoint resistance is close to 30 ohms and the reactance is near zero on 10 meters and quite low on 15 meters.

As operation is shifted to the lower bands, the antenna grows shorter in terms of operating wavelength and the feedpoint resistance drops accordingly. At the same time, antenna reactance rises and operating bandwidth decreases. At 80 meters, for example, the feedpoint resistance of the whip is about 0.5 ohm, the reactance has increased to over -1800 ohms and the operating bandwidth (defined as the operating range over which the feedline SWR is less than 2-to-1) has dropped to about 15 kHz.

For proper operation, the feedpoint resistance of the whip must be matched to 50 ohms and the negative reactance cancelled out by adding equal positive reactance in the form of a loading coil.

The Loading Coil

Experiments have shown that mounting the coil near the center of the antenna is a good compromise between electrical efficiency and mechanical awkwardness. The coil must have a high ratio of reactance to resistance to minimize coil loss. This means winding the coil with heavy wire on a form whose length is about two to four times the diameter. An air-wound coil, or one wound on a ceramic or polystyrene form, is recommended. A good coil will have a figure of merit (Q) of 300 or better. Even so, antenna efficiency is quite low.

For example, assume an 80 meter center loaded whip has a feedpoint resistance of 0.5 ohm and a reactance of -1850 ohms. The loading coil therefore must have a reactance of +1850 ohms to establish antenna resonance. If the coil has a Q of 300, the rf resistance of the coil is 1850/300, or about 6.2 ohms. Overall antenna efficiency is the feedpoint resistance divided by the sum of the coil resistance plus the feedpoint resistance: 0.5/(6.2+0.5), or .074 or 7.4 percent. This means that a 100 watt transmitter connected to this antenna would radiate about 7.4 watts!

It is very difficult to obtain a practical loading coil for 80 meters having a Q higher than about 300, so this is an example of a limiting case, so far as efficiency goes.

On 160 meters, the situation is even bleaker, as whip antenna efficiency runs about 0.5 percent. Even with this handicap, 160 meter mobile operation is practical and enjoyed by many amateurs.

Loading coil efficiency is much better on the higher bands and overall antenna efficiency is greater than 50 percent on the 20, 15 and 10 meter bands.

Tuning the HF Mobile Antenna

A good match between the mobile antenna and the coax feedline can be achieved with a shunt base coil, as described earlier. Before the coil and feedline are attached, the antenna should be grounded to the frame of the vehicle via a two turn loop and checked for resonance with a dip meter. The antenna is resonated to frequency by varying the number of turns in the loading coil or by adjusting the length of the top portion of the whip.

The antenna is now attached to the feedline and the shunt matching coil is placed across the coax line terminals. A tapped coil consisting of 20 turns, 1.5 inches (3.8 cm) in diameter is satisfactory. Low power is applied to the antenna and the number of turns on the coil adjusted to provide a low value of SWR on the feedline. It will be necessary to readjust the antenna slightly to reestablish resonance when the match is close to unity.

An easy way to temporarily lower the antenna resonant frequency is to add a few inches of wire at the top of the antenna with the aid of a copper battery clip. This is a quick and effective way of changing antenna resonance when the operating frequency is changed.

The VHF Mobile Antenna

The 1/4- and 3/8-wave vertical whip antennas are widely used for vhf mobile operation. A good match is achieved by feeding the antenna directly with a coax line. If the match needs to be improved, a small shunt coil can be placed across the antenna feedpoint. A six turn coil, 0.5 inch (1.3 cm) diameter about 1 inch (2.54 cm) long can do the job. Expand or squeeze the turns until the best match is achieved.

The ideal antenna mounting spot is on the roof of the car, with a rear-deck mount a good alternative. For temporary operation a magnetic mount can be used, although it can slip and let the antenna blow off the vehicle at high speeds, particularly when driving into a strong wind. A more permanent mount involves attaching the antenna base directly to the vehicle. Many amateurs hesitate to do this because it involves cutting a hole in the car body.

The Vertical Antenna-The Final Word by W6SAI

Many years ago a good friend described a vertical antenna to me as "one that radiates equally poorly in all directions". I believed that remark for many years until I had the opportunity to build and test various vertical antennas myself.

Looking back upon this story, I realized my friend was comparing a ground-mounted ground plane against a high, 3-element Yagi. The ground plane, moreover, was surrounded by power lines and close to adjacent buildings.

Why not give the vertical antenna a real chance to perform? My first vertical was a 50 foot, center-loaded whip for 80 meters. It was mounted atop a single story garage and had five radials which ran around the yard. It was a great DX antenna! I admit that within a thousand miles, it produced poor results. But working the east coast from W6-land, it provided reports equivalent to other local stations running high dipoles. And in Europe, Africa and Asia it excelled. I could hear DX stations other antennas could not pull out of the background. And my reports were impressive.

A series of follow-up verticals for the higher bands were built and used, always with good results. My conclusions, based upon using these simple and inexpensive antennas, were that--given a good chance--the vertical is a good antenna for the amateur with a lean purse and insufficient room to put up a beam.

Acknowledgements

The authors wish to thank the editors of "Ham Radio", "CQ" and "QST" magazines for permission to summarize certain selected articles for inclusion in this handbook. Thanks are also extended to the amateurs who designed the antennas shown in this Handbook for the benefit of their fellow amateurs.

OTHER BOOKS FROM RADIO AMATEUR CALLBOOK

All About Cubical Quad Antennas, by William Orr and Stuart Cowan; 112 pages. Data from A to Z, including expanded Quad. Building and tuning data. Gain figures. Multiband Quads. Delta Loop. "Monster Quads." Quad vs. Yagi. ISBN 0-8230-8703-4; $11.95.

Beam Antenna Handbook, by William Orr and Stuart Cowan; 271 pages. Latest edition contains computerized dimensions for popular Yagi beams (6 through 40 meters); data on triband and compact beams. Dimensional charts. Baluns. All you need to know to make your beam work. ISBN 0-8230-8704-2; $11.95.

Interference Handbook, 2d edition, by William Nelson, WA6FQG; 247 pages. Radio interference problems and solutions. Case histories. Power line noise, stereo interference, TVI, CATV, and more. ISBN 0-8230-8709-3; $11.95.

The Radio Amateur Antenna Handbook, by William Orr and Stuart Cowan; 192 pages. How to build popular antenna types: vertical and horizontal, beams, slopers. Compact antennas. How antenna location affects results. ISBN 0-8230-8706-9; $11.95.

Simple, Low-Cost Wire Antennas for Radio Amateurs, by William Orr and Stuart Cowan; 192 pages. How to build inexpensive, tested wire antennas, 2 through 160 meters. "Invisible" antennas for hams in "tough" locations. Multiband antennas. Wire beams. Tuners. Baluns. ISBN 0-8230-8707-7; $11.95.

Radio Amateur Callbooks are available at better electronics dealers and bookstores everywhere. See your nearest dealer or write for a free catalog:

RADIO AMATEUR CALLBOOK
P.O. Box 2013, Lakewood, New Jersey 08701